Elaine N. Marieb • Susan J. Mitchell

Human Anatomy & Physiology Laboratory Manual

Custom Edition for Broward College - Central Campus
Volume 2

Taken from:
Human Anatomy & Physiology Laboratory Manual, Tenth Edition
by Elaine N. Marieb and Susan J. Mitchell

D1364687

Cover image: Courtesy of Photodisc/Getty Images.

Taken from:

Human Anatomy & Physiology Laboratory Manual, Tenth Edition
by Elaine N. Marieb and Susan J. Mitchell
Copyright © 2011, 2008, 2006 by Pearson Education, Inc.
Published by Benjamin Cummings
San Francisco, California 94111

This special edition published in cooperation with Pearson Learning Solutions.

All trademarks, service marks, registered trademarks, and registered service marks are the property of their respective owners and are used herein for identification purposes only.

Pearson Learning Solutions, 501 Boylston Street, Suite 900, Boston, MA 02116
A Pearson Education Company
www.pearsoned.com

Printed in the United States of America

1 2 3 4 5 6 7 8 9 10 V0ZN 16 15 14 13 12 11

000200010270777535

KB

ISBN 10: 1-256-17056-9
ISBN 13: 978-1-256-17056-3

Contents

Preface to the Instructor

The philosophy behind the tenth edition of this manual mirrors that of all earlier editions. It reflects a still-developing sensibility for the way teachers teach and students learn, engendered by years of teaching the subject and by listening to the suggestions of other instructors as well as those of students enrolled in multifaceted health-care programs. *Human Anatomy & Physiology Laboratory Manual, Fetal Pig Version* was originally developed to facilitate and enrich the laboratory experience for both teachers and students. This, its tenth edition, retains those same goals.

This manual, intended for students in introductory human anatomy and physiology courses, presents a wide range of laboratory experiences for students concentrating in nursing, physical therapy, dental hygiene, pharmacology, respiratory therapy, and health and physical education, as well as biology and premedical programs. It differs from *Human Anatomy & Physiology Laboratory Manual, Main Version* (Ninth Edition, 2011) in that it contains detailed guidelines for dissecting a laboratory animal. The manual's coverage is intentionally broad, allowing it to serve both one- and two-semester courses.

BASIC APPROACH AND FEATURES

The generous variety of experiments in this manual provides flexibility that enables instructors to gear their laboratory approach to specific academic programs, or to their own teaching preferences. The manual is still independent of any textbook, so it contains the background discussions and terminology necessary to perform all experiments. Such a self-contained learning aid eliminates the need for students to bring a textbook into the laboratory.

Each of the 46 exercises leads students toward a coherent understanding of the structure and function of the human body. The manual begins with anatomical terminology and an orientation to the body, which together provide the necessary tools for studying the various body systems. The exercises that follow reflect the dual focus of the manual—both anatomical and physiological aspects receive considerable attention. As the various organ systems of the body are introduced, the initial exercises focus on organization, from the cellular to the organ system level. As indicated by the table of contents, the anatomical exercises are usually followed by physiological experiments that familiarize students with various aspects of body functioning and promote the critical understanding that function follows structure. Homeostasis is continually emphasized as a requirement for optimal health. Pathological conditions are viewed as a loss of homeostasis; these discussions can be recognized by the homeostatic imbalance logo within the descriptive material of each exercise. This holistic approach encourages an integrated understanding of the human body.

Features

- The numerous physiological experiments for each organ system range from simple experiments that can be performed without specialized tools to more complex experiments using laboratory equipment, computers, and instrumentation techniques.

- The laboratory Review Sheets following each exercise are designed to accompany that lab exercise. The Review Sheets provide space for recording and interpreting experimental results and require students to label diagrams and answer multiple-choice and short-answer questions.

- In addition to the figures, isolated animal organs such as the sheep heart and pig kidney are employed because of their exceptional similarity to human organs.

- All exercises involving body fluids (blood, urine, saliva) incorporate current Centers for Disease Control and Prevention (CDC) guidelines for handling human body fluids. Because it is important that nursing students, in particular, learn how to safely handle bloodstained articles, the human focus has been retained. However, the decision to allow testing of human (student) blood or to use animal blood in the laboratory is left to the discretion of the instructor in accordance with institutional guidelines. The CDC guidelines for handling body fluids are reinforced by the laboratory safety procedures described on the inside front cover of this text, in Exercise 29A: Blood, and in the *Instructor Guide*. You can photocopy the inside front cover and post it in the lab to help students become well versed in laboratory safety.

- Six logos alert students to special features or instructions. These include:

The dissection scissors icon appears at the beginning of activities that entail the dissection of isolated animal organs.

The homeostatic imbalance icon directs the student's attention to conditions representing a loss of homeostasis.

A safety icon notifies students that specific safety precautions must be observed when using certain equipment or conducting particular lab procedures. (For example, when working with ether, a hood is to be used, or when handling body fluids such as blood, urine, or saliva, gloves are to be worn.)

BIOPAC The BIOPAC icon in the materials list for an exercise clearly identifies use of the BIOPAC Student Lab System and alerts you to the equipment needed. BIOPAC is used in Exercises 16A, 20, 21, 22, 31, 33A, 34A, and 37A. The instructions in the lab manual are for use with the BIOPAC MP36 (or MP35/30) data acquisition unit. New versions of the BSL software (3.7.5 and higher for Windows, 3.7.4 and higher for Mac OS X) require different channel settings and collection strategies. Instructions for their use can be found in the Instructor Resources at myA&P. There you can also find instructions for the use of the new 2-channel data acquisition unit, the MP45.

PEx The PhysioEx icon at the end of the materials list for an exercise directs students to the corresponding PhysioEx computer simulation exercise found in the back of the lab manual.

• Other data aquisition instructions are available on myA&P, including:

PowerLab Instructions

For Exercises 16A, 22, 31, 33A, 34A, and 37A, instructors using PowerLab equipment may print these exercises for student handouts.

iWorx Instructions

For Exercises 16A, 20, 22, 31, 33A, 34A, and 37A, instructors using iWorx equipment in their laboratory may print these exercises for student handouts.

Intelitool Instructions

Four physiological experiments (Exercises 16i, 22i, 31i, and 37i) using Intelitool® equipment are available. Instructors using Intelitool equipment in their laboratory may print these exercises for student handouts.

WHAT'S NEW

In this revision, we have continued to try to respond to reviewers' and users' feedback concerning trends that are having an impact on the anatomy and physiology laboratory experience, most importantly:

• The growing demand for student-based experimentation

• The increased use of computers in the laboratory and in students' homes, and hence the continuing desire for more computer simulation and practice exercises

• The replacement of older recording equipment with computerized data acquisition and analysis systems

• The continued importance of visual learning for today's student

• The need to reinforce writing, computation, and critical thinking skills across the curriculum

The specific changes implemented to address these trends are described next.

Pre-lab Quizzes

Brand new pre-lab quizzes at the beginning of each Exercise motivate your students to prepare for lab by asking them basic information they should know before doing the lab. These quizzes are different than those found on myA&P and those in the Instuctor Test Bank.

All-new Art Program

This brand-new art program uses three-dimensional, realistic styles with dramatic views and perspectives, and rich, vibrant colors. The art includes key anatomy figures that are rendered with detail, depth, and a clear focus on key anatomical structures. Ten new and improved histology images have been added. Images from the Histology Atlas have been integrated into the lab exercises so that students can review relevant histology images all in one place. See page vi for a complete listing of histology figures.

Also included are five new cadaver photos and all new surface anatomy photos showing superb muscle definition and clear surface landmarks for skeletal, muscular, and vascular structures.

New! Electronic Test Bank of Pre-lab and Post-lab Quizzes

See "Supplements for the Instructor" on page xi.

Customization Options

With Integrate, our custom laboratory publishing program for anatomy and physiology, you have the freedom to choose labs from our library of highly regarded Pearson Benjamin Cummings lab manuals and other collections to build the right manual for your course. You'll find excellent, class-tested labs—many printed in full color—for one- and two-semester anatomy and physiology laboratories, and one-semester human anatomy or physiology courses. Use our online Book-Build system to select just the labs you need, in the sequence you want—your students pay only for the labs you choose. You can also add your own original labs. With Integrate, you're in control. For more information, visit our Integrate website at www.pearsoncustom/integrate, or contact your Pearson sales representative for details.

SUPPLEMENTS FOR THE STUDENT

Practice Anatomy Lab 2.0

Practice Anatomy Lab (PAL) 2.0 is an indispensable virtual anatomy study and practice tool that gives students 24/7 access to the most widely used lab specimens including **human cadaver, anatomical models, histology, cat, and fetal pig.**
    PAL 2.0 features:

• **Hundreds of images** and interactive tools for reviewing and learning the names of anatomical structures

• **Built-in audio pronunciation** of anatomical terms

• Rich variety of **multiple choice quizzes** and **fill-in-the-blank lab practical exams**

- **3D anatomy animations** of origins, insertions, actions, and innervations of over 65 muscles in the Human Cadaver module
- **Fully rotatable human skull** and 17 other rotatable skeletal structures

The Instructor's Resource DVD for PAL 2.0 includes labeled and unlabeled images from PAL 2.0 in both JPEG and PowerPoint® formats. The PowerPoint Label Edit feature, with editable labels and leader lines, is built into every image. PowerPoint image slides include embedded links to the relevant 3D animations of origins, insertions, actions, and innervations.

PAL 2.0 is available on the myA&P Lab Manual Website at www.myaandp.com. The PAL 2.0 CD-ROM can also be packaged with Marieb's lab manual at no additional charge.

PhysioEx 8.0 CD-ROM

The PhysioEx CD-ROM, packaged with every lab manual, consists of 11 modules containing 79 physiology lab simulations that may be used to supplement or substitute for wet labs. PhysioEx 8.0 allows you to repeat labs as often as you like, perform simulated animal experiments and conduct simulated wet lab experiments either in or out of the laboratory.

PhysioEx 8.0 also includes videos of laboratory experiments that demonstrate the actual experiments simulated on the screen, making it easier for students to understand and visualize the laboratory context of the simulations. The seven videos demonstrate the following experiments: Skeletal Muscle, Blood Typing, Cardiovascular Physiology, Use of a Water-Filled Spirometer, Nerve Impulses, BMR Measurement, and Cell Transport.

Unlike the typical tutorial-based computer supplements that usually target anatomy, the 79 physiology activities on PhysioEx 8.0 allow students to explore using variable parameters while being guided through the process of discovery in a laboratory exercise. Particularly advantageous is the fact that the students can conduct or review the experiments and slides at home on a personal computer. PhysioEx 8.0 also provides convenient "laboratory access" for students enrolled in Internet-based distance education courses and is available online at the companion website for this lab manual at myA&P. (Use the access code found at the front of your lab manual to log onto the site.)

PhysioEx 8.0 topics include:

- Exercise 5B, *Cell Transport Mechanisms and Permeability: Computer Simulation.* Explores how substances cross the cell's membrane. Simple and facilitated diffusion, osmosis, filtration, and active transport are covered.
- Exercise 6B, *Histology Atlas and Review Supplement.* Includes over 200 histology images, viewable at various magnifications, with accompanying descriptions and labels.

- Exercise 16B, *Skeletal Muscle Physiology: Computer Simulation.* Provides insights into the complex physiology of skeletal muscle. Electrical stimulation, isometric contractions, and isotonic contractions are investigated.
- Exercise 18B, *Neurophysiology of Nerve Impulses: Computer Simulation.* Investigates stimuli that elicit action potentials, stimuli that inhibit action potentials, and factors affecting nerve conduction velocity.
- Exercise 28B, *Endocrine System Physiology: Computer Simulation.* Investigates the relationship between hormones and metabolism; the effect of estrogen replacement therapy; the diagnosis of diabetes; and the relationship between the levels of cortisol and adrenocorticotropic hormone and a variety of endocrine disorders.
- Exercise 29B, *Blood Analysis: Computer Simulation.* Covers hematocrit determination, erythrocyte sedimentation rate determination, hemoglobin determination, blood typing, and total cholesterol determination.
- Exercise 33B, *Cardiovascular Dynamics: Computer Simulation.* Allows students to perform experiments that would be difficult if not impossible to do in a traditional laboratory. Topics of inquiry include vessel resistance and pump (heart) mechanics.
- Exercise 34B, *Frog Cardiovascular Physiology: Computer Simulation.* Variables influencing heart activity are examined. Topics include setting up and recording baseline heart activity, the refractory period of cardiac muscle, and an investigation of factors that affect heart rate and contractility.
- Exercise 35B, *Serological Testing: Computer Simulation* **(available online only at myA&P).** Investigates antigen-antibody reactions and their role in clinical tests used to diagnose a disease or an infection.
- Exercise 37B, *Respiratory System Mechanics: Computer Simulation.* Investigates physical and chemical aspects of pulmonary function. Students collect data simulating normal lung volumes. Other activities examine factors such as airway resistance and the effect of surfactant on lung function.
- Exercise 39B, *Chemical and Physical Processes of Digestion: Computer Simulation.* Turns the student's computer into a virtual chemistry lab where enzymes, reagents, and incubation conditions can be manipulated (in compressed time) to examine factors that affect enzyme activity.
- Exercise 41B, *Renal System Physiology: Computer Simulation.* Simulates the function of a single nephron. Topics include factors influencing glomerular filtration, the effect of hormones on urine function, and glucose transport maximum.
- Exercise 47, *Acid-Base Balance: Computer Simulation.* Topics include respiratory and metabolic acidosis/alkalosis, and renal and respiratory compensation.

myA&P

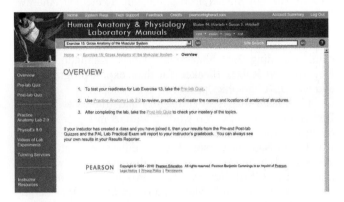

From the home page of myA&P (www.myaandp.com), you and your students can access the companion website for the Human Anatomy & Physiology Laboratory Manuals, which features the following resources and activities:

- **Access to Practice Anatomy Lab 2.0**

- **Gradable pre- and post-lab quizzes** for each of the 46 lab exercises in the lab manual. These quizzes are different than those found in the lab manual.

- **PhysioEx 8.0**

Instructor tools:

- **Gradebook** allows pre- and post-lab quizzes and PAL Lab Practical Exams to be reported to the instructor's online gradebook.

- **Instructor Resources** include the Instructor Guide, procedures for using **PowerLab®, iWorx®,** and **Intelitool®** equipment with certain lab exercises, and more.

A 12-month subscription to this powerful website is included with each new copy of the lab manual. Access directions, along with access codes, are included at the front of the book.

Also Available

A Brief Atlas of the Human Body, Second Edition (0-321-66261-X)

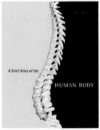

This full-color atlas includes 107 bone and 47 soft-tissue photographs with easy-to-read labels. This edition of the atlas contains a brand-new, comprehensive histology photomicrograph section with more than 50 slides of basic tissue and organ systems. Featuring photos taken by renowned biomedical photographer Ralph Hutchings, this high-quality photographic atlas makes an excellent resource for the classroom and laboratory. Available for purchase from Pearson Education.

SUPPLEMENTS FOR THE INSTRUCTOR

New! Electronic Test Bank of Pre-lab and Post-lab Quizzes

This brand-new electronic Test Bank of pre-lab and post-lab quizzes, different than those found in the lab manual and on myA&P, allows you to assign these quizzes for homework or extra credit. These quizzes can be downloaded from the Instructor Resources section of my A&P and imported into **WebCT, BlackBoard, CourseCompass,** and other course-management systems.

New! PAL 2.0 IRDVD with Updated Test Bank

This DVD includes everything you need to present and assign PAL 2.0 in your lecture and lab. Whether it's used for lecture presentation, pre-lab assignments, or testing, this invaluable resource makes it easy for you to use PAL 2.0 to fit *your* course.

The IRDVD with Updated Test Bank for PAL 2.0 includes:

- Additional images of specimens not found in PAL 2.0

- Embedded 3D anatomy animations and bone rotations in relevant PowerPoint slides

- Active Lecture Questions (for use with or without clickers)

- Index of anatomical structures covered in PAL 2.0

- Updated Test Bank allows you to modify multiple-choice quiz questions and fill-in-the-blank lab practical questions to reflect the content you want your students to be quizzed and tested on. Test Bank includes more than 3400 questions. Available in PDF and TestGen format. Test item files can be imported into **WebCT, Blackboard,** and **CourseCompass.**

myA&P Instructor Resources

Instructor Resources include the Instructor Guide, procedures for using **PowerLab®, iWorx®,** and **Intelitool®** equipment with certain lab exercises, and instructions for BIOPAC exercises using the newest software (3.7.5 for Windows and 3.7.4 for Mac) and data acquisition unit (MP45).

Instructor Guide (0-321-64415-8)

This guide accompanies all versions of the *Human Anatomy & Physiology Laboratory Manual* and contains a wealth of information for those teaching this course, including answers to the new pre-lab quizzes. Instructors can find help in planning the experiments, ordering equipment and supplies, anticipating pitfalls and problem areas, and locating audiovisual material. The probable in-class time required for each lab is indicated by an hourglass icon. Another useful resource is the Trends in Instrumentation section, which describes the latest laboratory equipment and technological teaching tools available.

Human Anatomy & Physiology Videotapes

These tapes are available free of charge to qualified adopters. Produced by University Media Services and scripted by Rose Leigh Vines, Rosalee Carter, and Ann Motekaitis of California State University, Sacramento, these excellent videotapes reinforce many of the concepts covered in this manual and represent a valuable addition to any multimedia library.

Student Video Series Vol. I (0-8053-4110-2)

Student Video Series Vol. II (0-8053-6115-4)

ACKNOWLEDGMENTS

We wish to thank the following reviewers for their contributions to this edition: C. Thomas G. Appleton, University of Western Ontario; Richard Connett, Monroe Community College; Smruti Desai, Lone Star College CyFair; Jose Fierro, Florida State College at Jacksonville; Katelijne Flies, Central New Mexico Community College; Lynn Gargan, Tarrant County College Northeast; Lori Garrett, Parkland College; Fran Hardin, Ivy Tech Community College—Kokomo; DJ Hennager, Kirkwood Community College; William Hoover, Bunker Hill Community College; Sandra Hsu, Skyline College; William Huber, St. Louis Community College; Jesse Lang, Holyoke Community College; Stephen Lebsack, Linn Benton Community College; Linda Mackie, St. Johns River Community College; Cherie McKeever, Montana State University—Great Falls, College of Technology; Judy Megaw, Indian River Community College; Ellen Ott-Reeves, Blinn Community College; Steve Perry, Liberty University; Jean Revie, South Mountain Community College; Laura Ritt, Burlington Community College; Josephine Rogers, University of Cincinnati; Dale Smoak, Piedmont Technical College; Pam Strong, Quincy College; Diane Teter, South Texas College; Harriett Tresham, Kennesaw Community College; Maureen Tubbiola, St. Cloud State; Wendy Waters, Wharton Junior College.

We would like to extend a special thank you to the following authors of our outstanding companion website and Practice Anatomy Lab 2.0: Ruth Heisler, University of Colorado; Nora Hebert, Red Rocks Community College; Yvonne Baptiste-Szymanski, Niagara County Community College; Deanna Denault, New Hampshire Community Technical College—Claremont; Steve Downing, University of Minnesota Medical School—Duluth; Marjorie Johnson, University of Western Ontario; Leif Saul, University of Colorado; Charles J. Venglarik, Jefferson State Community College; and Nina Zanetti, Siena College.

Special thanks to Josephine Rogers of the University of Cincinnati for authoring the brand new pre-lab quizzes featured in this edition of the lab manual.

The excellence of PhysioEx reflects the expertise of Peter Zao, Timothy Stabler, Lori Smith, Greta Peterson, Andrew Lokuta, and Nina Zanetti. They generated the ideas behind the equipment graphics and envisioned the animations that would be needed. Credit also goes to the team at Cadre Design, including Ian Shakeshaft, Chris Kemmett, David Hegarty, and Robert Bleeker, for their expert programming and wonderful graphics produced in PhysioEx.

Continued thanks to colleagues and friends at Pearson Benjamin Cummings who worked with us in the production of this edition, especially Serina Beauparlant, Editor-in-Chief, and Sabrina Larson, Project Editor, who efficiently shepherded the manuscript every millimeter of the way. Applause also to Erik Fortier, Media Producer, who managed PhysioEx and myA&P. Many thanks to Stacey Weinberger for her manufacturing expertise. Finally, our Marketing Manager, Derek Perrigo, has efficiently kept us in touch with the pulse of the market place.

Kudos also to Michele Mangelli and her production team, who did their usual great job. Janet Vail, production editor for this project, got the job done in jig time. Laura Southworth, Art Development Manager, and Karen Gulliver, Art Editor, were in charge of overseeing the entire art program. Jean Lake acted as art and photo coordinator, and Kristin Piljay conducted photo research. Our fabulous interior and cover designs were created by Yvo Riezebos. Antonio Padial brought his experience to copyediting the text.

We are grateful to the team at BIOPAC, especially to Jocelyn Kremer, who was extremely helpful in making sure we had the latest updates and answering all of our questions.

Last but not least, thank you to Robert Sullivan of Marist College for authoring the rat dissection exercises found in the brand-new Rat Version of this lab manual.

[signatures]

Elaine N. Marieb and
Susan J. Mitchell
Anatomy and Physiology
Pearson Benjamin Cummings
1301 Sansome Street
San Francisco, CA 94111

We hope you will enjoy your laboratory experiences. As with any unfamiliar experience, it really helps if you know in advance what to expect and what will be expected of you.

LABORATORY ACTIVITIES

The A&P laboratory exercises in this manual are designed to help you gain a broad understanding of both anatomy and physiology. You can anticipate examining models, dissecting a specimen, and using a microscope to look at tissue slides (anatomical approaches). You will also investigate chemical interactions in both living and nonliving systems, manipulate variables in computer simulations, and conduct experiments that examine responses of living organisms to various stimuli (physiological approaches).

Preserved organ specimens used in the anatomy and physiology labs are *not* harvested from animals raised specifically for dissection purposes. Organs that are of no use to the meat packing industry (such as the brain, heart, or lungs) are sent from slaughterhouses to biological supply houses for preparation.

Included with this edition is a companion website designed to help you practice for lab practical exams outside of class. Also included with the manual is the PhysioEx CD-ROM, with 11 simulation exercises that allow you to convert a computer into a virtual laboratory. You will be able to manipulate variables to investigate physiological phenomena.

There is little doubt that computer simulations offer many advantages, however an animated frog muscle or heart on a computer screen is not really a substitute for observing the responses of actual muscle tissue. Consequently, living animal experiments remain an important part of the approach of this manual to the study of human anatomy and physiology. However, we use the minimum number of animals needed.

If you use living animals for experiments, you are required to handle them humanely. Inconsiderate treatment of laboratory animals will not be tolerated in your anatomy and physiology laboratory.

ICONS/VISUAL MNEMONICS

We have tried to make this manual easy for you to use by employing different icons (visual mnemonics) throughout:

The *Dissection* head is orange and is accompanied by the **dissection scissors icon** at the beginning of activities that require you to dissect isolated animal organs.

The **homeostatic imbalance icon** directs your attention to conditions representing a disruption of homeostasis.

The **safety icon** alerts you to special precautions that you should take when handling lab equipment or conducting certain procedures. For example, it alerts you to use a ventilating hood when using volatile chemicals and signifies that you should take special measures to protect yourself when handling blood or other body fluids (e.g., saliva, urine).

BIOPAC® The **BIOPAC icon** in the materials list for an exercise clearly identifies use of the BIOPAC Student Lab System. BIOPAC is used in Exercises 16A, 20, 21, 22, 31, 33A, 34A, and 37A.

PEx The **PhysioEx icon** at the end of the materials list for an exercise directs you to the corresponding PhysioEx computer simulation exercise found in the back of the lab manual.

HINTS FOR SUCCESS
IN THE LABORATORY

Most students can use helpful hints and guidelines to ensure that they have successful lab experiences.

1. Perhaps the best bit of advice is to attend all your scheduled labs and to participate in all the assigned exercises. Learning is an *active* process.

2. Scan the scheduled lab exercise and the questions in the Review Sheet following it *before* going to lab, then complete the pre-lab quiz.

3. Be on time. Most instructors explain what the lab is about, pitfalls to avoid, and the sequence or format to be followed at the beginning of the lab session. If you are late, not only will you miss this information, you also will not endear yourself to the instructor.

4. Follow the instructions in the order in which they are given. If you do not understand a direction, ask for help.

5. Review your lab notes after completing the lab session to help you focus on and remember the important concepts.

6. Keep your work area clean and neat. Move books and coats out of the way. This reduces confusion and accidents.

7. Assume that all lab chemicals and equipment are sources of potential danger to you. Follow directions for equipment use and observe the laboratory safety guidelines provided inside the front cover of this manual.

8. Keep in mind the real value of the laboratory experience— a place for you to observe, manipulate, and experience hands-on activities that will dramatically enhance your understanding of the lecture presentations.

We hope that this lab manual makes learning about intricate structures and functions of the human body a fun and rewarding process. We are always open to constructive criticism and suggestions for improvement in future editions. If you have any, please write to us.

Elaine N. Marieb and
Susan J. Mitchell
Anatomy and Physiology
Pearson Benjamin Cummings
1301 Sansome Street
San Francisco, CA 94111

Getting Started—What to Expect, The Scientific Method, and Metrics

Two hundred years ago science was largely a plaything of wealthy patrons, but today's world is dominated by science and its technology. Whether or not we believe that such domination is desirable, we all have a responsibility to try to understand the goals and methods of science that have seeded this knowledge and technological explosion.

The biosciences are very special and exciting because they open the doors to an understanding of all the wondrous workings of living things. A course in human anatomy and physiology (a minute subdivision of bioscience) provides such insights in relation to your own body. Although some experience in scientific studies is helpful when beginning a study of anatomy and physiology, perhaps the single most important prerequisite is curiosity.

Gaining an understanding of science is a little like becoming acquainted with another person. Even though a written description can provide a good deal of information about the person, you can never really know another unless there is personal contact. And so it is with science—if you are to know it well, you must deal with it intimately.

The laboratory is the setting for "intimate contact" with science. It is where scientists test their ideas (do research), the essential purpose of which is to provide a basis from which predictions about scientific phenomena can be made. Likewise, it will be the site of your "intimate contact" with the subject of human anatomy and physiology as you are introduced to the methods and instruments used in biological research.

For many students, human anatomy and physiology is taken as an introductory-level course; and their scientific background exists, at best, as a dim memory. If this is your predicament, this prologue may be just what you need to fill in a few gaps and to get you started on the right track before your actual laboratory experiences begin. So—let's get to it!

THE SCIENTIFIC METHOD

Science would quickly stagnate if new knowledge were not continually derived from and added to it. The approach commonly used by scientists when they investigate various aspects of their respective disciplines is called the **scientific method.** This method is *not* a single rigorous technique that must be followed in a lockstep manner. It is nothing more or less than a logical, practical, and reliable way of approaching and solving problems of every kind—scientific or otherwise—to gain knowledge. It comprises five major steps.

Step 1: Observation of Phenomena

The crucial first step involves observation of some phenomenon of interest. In other words, before a scientist can investigate anything, he or she must decide on a *problem* or focus for the investigation. In most college laboratory experiments, the problem or focus has been decided for you. However, to illustrate this important step, we will assume that you want to investigate the true nature of apples, particularly green apples. In such a case you would begin your studies by making a number of different observations concerning apples.

Step 2: Statement of the Hypothesis

Once you have decided on a focus of concern, the next step is to design a significant question to be answered. Such a question is usually posed in the form of a **hypothesis,** an unproven conclusion that attempts to explain some phenomenon. (At its crudest level, a hypothesis can be considered to be a "guess" or an intuitive hunch that tentatively explains some observation.) Generally, scientists do not restrict themselves to a single hypothesis; instead, they usually pose several and then test each one systematically.

We will assume that, to accomplish step 1, you go to the supermarket and randomly select apples from several bins. When you later eat the apples, you find that the green apples are sour, but the red and yellow apples are sweet. From this observation, you might conclude *(hypothesize)* that "green apples are sour." This statement would represent your current understanding of green apples. You might also reasonably predict that if you were to buy more apples, any green ones you buy will be sour. Thus, you would have gone beyond your initial observation that "these" green apples are sour to the prediction that "all" green apples are sour.

Any good hypothesis must meet several criteria. First, *it must be testable*. This characteristic is far more important than its being correct. The test data may or may not support the hypothesis, or new information may require that the hypothesis be modified. Clearly the accuracy of a prediction in any scientific study depends on the accuracy of the initial information on which it is based.

In our example, no great harm will come from an inaccurate prediction—that is, were we to find that some green apples are sweet. However, in some cases human life may depend on the accuracy of the prediction; thus: (1) Repeated testing of scientific ideas is important, particularly because scientists working on the same problem do not always agree in their conclusions. (2) Careful observation is essential, even at the very outset of a study, because conclusions drawn from scientific tests are only as accurate as the information on which they are based.

A second criterion is that, even though hypotheses are guesses of a sort, *they must be based on measurable, describable facts. No mysticism can be theorized.* We cannot conjure up, to support our hypothesis, forces that have not been shown to exist. For example, as scientists, we cannot say that the tooth fairy took Johnny's tooth unless we can prove that the tooth fairy exists!

Third, a hypothesis *must not be anthropomorphic*. Human beings tend to anthropomorphize—that is, to relate all experiences to human experience. Whereas we could state that bears instinctively protect their young, it would be anthropomorphic to say that bears love their young, because love is a human emotional response. Thus, the initial hypothesis must be stated without interpretation.

Step 3: Data Collection

Once the initial hypothesis has been stated, scientists plan experiments that will provide data (or evidence) to support or disprove their hypotheses—that is, they *test* their hypotheses. Data are accumulated by making qualitative or quantitative observations of some sort. The observations are often aided by the use of various types of equipment such as cameras, microscopes, stimulators, or various electronic devices that allow chemical and physiological measurements to be taken.

Observations referred to as **qualitative** are those we can make with our senses—that is, by using our vision, hearing, or sense of taste, smell, or touch. For some quick practice in qualitative observation, compare and contrast* an orange and an apple.

Whereas the differences between an apple and an orange are obvious, this is not always the case in biological observations. Quite often a scientist tries to detect very subtle differences that cannot be determined by qualitative observations; data must be derived from measurements. Such observations based on precise measurements of one type or another are **quantitative observations**. Examples of quantitative observations include careful measurements of body or organ dimensions such as mass, size, and volume; measurement of volumes of oxygen consumed during metabolic studies; determination of the concentration of glucose in urine; and determination of the differences in blood pressure and pulse under conditions of rest and exercise. An apple and an orange could be compared quantitatively by analyzing the relative amounts of sugar and water in a given volume of fruit flesh, the pigments and vitamins present in the apple skin and orange peel, and so on.

A valuable part of data gathering is the use of experiments to support or disprove a hypothesis. An **experiment** is a procedure designed to describe the factors in a given situation that affect one another (that is, to discover cause and effect) under certain conditions.

Two general rules govern experimentation. The first of these rules is that the experiment(s) should be conducted in such a manner that every **variable** (any factor that might affect the outcome of the experiment) is under the control of the experimenter. The **independent variables** are manipulated by the experimenter. For example, if the goal is to determine the effect of body temperature on breathing rate, the independent variable is body temperature. The effect observed or value measured (in this case breathing rate) is called the **dependent** or **response variable**. Its value "depends" on the value chosen for the independent variable. The ideal way to perform such an experiment is to set up and run a series of tests that are all identical, except for one specific factor that is varied.

One specimen (or group of specimens) is used as the **control** against which all other experimental samples are compared. The importance of the control sample cannot be overemphasized. The control group provides the "normal standard" against which all other samples are compared relative to the dependent variable. Taking our example one step further, if we wanted to investigate the effects of body temperature (the independent variable) on breathing rate (the dependent variable), we could collect data on the breathing rate of individuals with "normal" body temperature (the implicit control group), and compare these data to breathing-rate measurements obtained from groups of individuals with higher and lower body temperatures.

The second rule governing experimentation is that valid results require that testing be done on large numbers of subjects. It is essential to understand that it is nearly impossible to control all possible variables in biological tests. Indeed, there is a bit of scientific wisdom that mirrors this truth—that is, that laboratory animals, even in the most rigidly controlled and carefully designed experiments, "will do as they damn well please." Thus, stating that the testing of a drug for its painkilling effects was successful after having tested it on only one postoperative patient would be scientific suicide. Large numbers of patients would have to receive the drug and be monitored for a decrease in postoperative pain before such a statement could have any scientific validity. Then, other researchers would have to be able to uphold those conclusions by running similar experiments. *Repeatability* is an important part of the scientific method and is the primary basis for support or rejection of many hypotheses.

During experimentation and observation, data must be carefully recorded. Usually, such initial, or raw, data are recorded in table form. The table should be labeled to show the variables investigated and the results for each sample. At this point, *accurate recording* of observations is the primary concern. Later, these raw data will be reorganized and manipulated to show more explicitly the outcome of the experimentation.

Some of the observations that you will be asked to make in the anatomy and physiology laboratory will require that a drawing be made. Don't panic! The purpose of making drawings (in addition to providing a record) is to force you to observe things very closely. You need not be an artist (most biological drawings are simple outline drawings), but you do need to be neat and as accurate as possible. It is advisable to use a 4H pencil to do your drawings because it is easily erased and doesn't smudge. Before beginning to draw, you should examine your specimen closely, studying it as though you were going to have to draw it from memory. For example, when looking at cells you should ask yourself questions such as "What is their shape—the relationship of length and width? How are they joined together?" Then decide precisely what you are going to show and how large the drawing must be to show the necessary detail. After making the drawing, add labels in the margins and connect them by straight lines (leader lines) to the structures being named.

Step 4: Manipulation and Analysis of Data

The form of the final data varies, depending on the nature of the data collected. Usually, the final data represent information converted from the original measured values (raw data)

---

* *Compare* means to emphasize the similarities between two things, whereas *contrast* means that the differences are to be emphasized.

to some other form. This may mean that averaging or some other statistical treatment must be applied, or it may require conversions from one kind of units to another. In other cases, graphs may be needed to display the data.

Elementary Treatment of Data

Only very elementary statistical treatment of data is required in this manual. For example, you will be expected to understand and/or compute an average (mean), percentages, and a range.

Two of these statistics, the mean and the range, are useful in describing the *typical* case among a large number of samples evaluated. Let us use a simple example. We will assume that the following heart rates (in beats/min) were recorded during an experiment: 64, 70, 82, 94, 85, 75, 72, 78. If you put these numbers in numerical order, the **range** is easily computed, because the range is the difference between the highest and lowest numbers obtained (highest number minus lowest number). The **mean** is obtained by summing the items and dividing the sum by the number of items. What is the range and the mean for the set of numbers just provided?

1. _____ *

The word *percent* comes from the Latin meaning "for 100"; thus *percent,* indicated by the percent sign, %, means parts per 100 parts. Thus, if we say that 45% of Americans have type O blood, what we are really saying is that among each group of 100 Americans, 45 (45/100) can be expected to have type O blood. Any ratio can be converted to a percent by multiplying by 100 and adding the percent sign.

$$.25 \times 100 = 25\% \qquad 5 \times 100 = 500\%$$

It is very easy to convert any number (including decimals) to a percent. The rule is to move the decimal point two places to the right and add the percent sign. If no decimal point appears, it is *assumed* to be at the end of the number; and zeros are added to fill any empty spaces. Two examples follow:

$$0.25 = 0.25 = 25\%$$
$$5 = 5 = 500\%$$

Change the following to percents:

2. 38 = _____   **4.** 1.6 = _____

3. .75 = _____

Note that although you are being asked here to convert numbers to percents, percents by themselves are meaningless. We always speak in terms of a percentage *of* something.

To change a percent to decimal form, remove the percent sign, and divide by 100. Change the following percents to whole numbers or decimals:

5. 800% = _____   **6.** 0.05% = _____

Making and Reading Line Graphs

For some laboratory experiments you will be required to show your data (or part of them) graphically. Simple line graphs allow relationships within the data to be shown interestingly and allow trends (or patterns) in the data to be demonstrated. An advantage of properly drawn graphs is that they save the reader's time because the essential meaning of a large amount of statistical data can be seen at a glance.

To aid in making accurate graphs, graph paper (or a printed grid in the manual) is used. Line graphs have both horizontal (X) and vertical (Y) axes with scales. Each scale should have uniform intervals—that is, each unit measured on the scale should require the same distance along the scale as any other. Variations from this rule may be misleading and result in false interpretations of the data. By convention, the condition that is manipulated (the independent variable) in the experimental series is plotted on the X-axis (the horizontal axis); and the value that we then measure (the dependent variable) is plotted on the Y-axis (the vertical axis). To plot the data, a dot or a small **x** is placed at the precise point where the two variables (measured for each sample) meet; and then a line (this is called the **curve**) is drawn to connect the plotted points.

Sometimes, you will see the curve on a line graph extended beyond the last plotted point. This is (supposedly) done to predict "what comes next." When you see this done, be skeptical. The information provided by such a technique is only slightly more accurate than that provided by a crystal ball! When constructing a graph, be sure to label the X-axis and Y-axis and give the graph a legend (see Figure G.1).

To read a line graph, pick any point on the line, and match it with the information directly below on the X-axis and with that directly to the left of it on the Y-axis. Figure G.1 is a graph that illustrates the relationship between breaths per minute (respiratory rate) and body temperature. Answer the following questions about this graph:

7. What was the respiratory rate at a body temperature of 96°F? _____

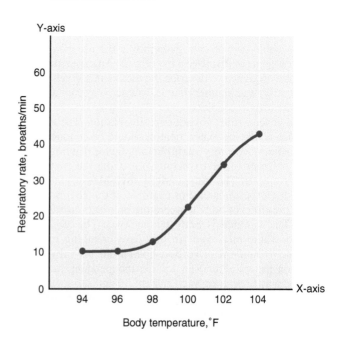

FIGURE G.1   Example of graphically presented data. Respiratory rate as a function of body temperature.

8. Between which two body temperature readings was the

increase in breaths per minute greatest? _____

Step 5: Reporting Conclusions of the Study

Drawings, tables, and graphs alone do not suffice as the final presentation of scientific results. The final step requires that you provide a straightforward description of the conclusions drawn from your results. If possible, your findings should be compared to those of other investigators working on the same problem. (For laboratory investigations conducted by students, these comparative figures are provided by classmates.)

It is important to realize that scientific investigations do not always yield the anticipated results. If there are discrepancies between your results and those of others, or what you expected to find based on your class notes or textbook readings, this is the place to try to explain those discrepancies.

Results are often only as good as the observation techniques used. Depending on the type of experiment conducted,

LAB REPORT

Cover Page

- Title of Experiment
- Author's Name
- Course
- Instructor
- Date

Introduction

- Provide background information.
- Describe any relevant observations.
- State hypotheses clearly.

Materials and Methods

- List equipment or supplies needed.
- Provide step-by-step directions for conducting the experiment.

Results

- Present data using a drawing (figure), table, or graph.
- Analyze data.
- Summarize findings briefly.

Discussion and Conclusions

- Conclude whether data gathered support or do not support hypotheses.
- Include relevant information from other sources.
- Explain any uncontrolled variables or unexpected difficulties.
- Make suggestions for further experimentation.

Reference List

- Cite the source of any material used to support this report.

you may need to answer several questions. Did you weigh the specimen carefully enough? Did you balance the scale first? Was the subject's blood pressure actually as high as you recorded it, or did you record it inaccurately? If you did record it accurately, is it possible that the subject was emotionally upset about something, which might have given falsely high data for the variable being investigated? Attempting to explain an unexpected result will often teach you more than you would have learned from anticipated results.

When the experiment produces results that are consistent with the hypothesis, then the hypothesis can be said to have reached a higher level of certainty. The probability that the hypothesis is correct is greater.

A hypothesis that has been validated by many different investigators is called a **theory.** Theories are useful in two important ways. First, they link sets of data; and second, they make predictions that may lead to additional avenues of investigation. (OK, we know this with a high degree of certainty; what's next?)

When a theory has been repeatedly verified and appears to have wide applicability in biology, it may assume the status of a **biological principle.** A principle is a statement that applies with a high degree of probability to a range of events. For example, "Living matter is made of cells or cell products" is a principle stated in many biology texts. It is a sound and useful principle, and will continue to be used as such—unless new findings prove it wrong.

We have been through quite a bit of background concerning the scientific method and what its use entails. Because it is important that you remember the phases of the scientific method, they are summarized here:

1. Observation of some phenomenon

2. Statement of a hypothesis (based on the observations)

3. Collection of data (testing the hypothesis with controlled experiments)

4. Manipulation and analysis of the data

5. Reporting of the conclusions of the study (routinely done by preparing a lab report—see page xvii)

Writing a Lab Report Based on the Scientific Method

A laboratory report is not the same as a scientific paper, but it has some of the same elements and is a formal way to report the results of a scientific experiment. The report should have a cover page that includes the title of the experiment, the author's name, the name of the course, the instructor, and the date. The report should include five separate, clearly marked sections: Introduction, Materials and Methods, Results, Discussion and Conclusions, and References. Use the previous template to guide you through writing a lab report.

METRICS

No matter how highly developed our ability to observe, observations have scientific value only if we can communicate them to others. Without measurement, we would be limited to qualitative description. For precise and repeatable communication of information, the agreed-upon system of measurement used by scientists is the **metric system.**

A major advantage of the metric system is that it is based on units of 10. This allows rapid conversion to workable numbers so that neither very large nor very small figures need be used in calculations. Fractions or multiples of the standard units of length, volume, mass, time, and temperature have been assigned specific names. Table G.1 shows the commonly used units of the metric system, along with the prefixes used to designate fractions and multiples thereof.

To change from smaller units to larger units, you must *divide* by the appropriate factor of 10 (because there are fewer of the larger units). For example, a milliunit (*milli* = one-thousandth), such as a millimeter, is one step smaller than a centiunit (*centi* = one-hundredth), such as a centimeter. Thus to change milliunits to centiunits, you must divide by 10. On the other hand, when converting from larger units to smaller ones, you must *multiply* by the appropriate factor of 10. A partial scheme for conversions between the metric units is shown on the next page.

TABLE G.1	Metric System			
A. Commonly used units		**B. Fractions and their multiples**		
Measurement	**Unit**	**Fraction or multiple**	**Prefix**	**Symbol**
Length	Meter (m)	10^6 one million	mega	M
Volume	Liter (L; l with prefix)	10^3 one thousand	kilo	k
Mass	Gram (g)	10^{-1} one-tenth	deci	d
Time*	Second (s)	10^{-2} one-hundredth	centi	c
Temperature	Degree Celsius (°C)	10^{-3} one-thousandth	milli	m
		10^{-6} one-millionth	micro	μ
		10^{-9} one-billionth	nano	n

* The accepted standard for time is the second; and thus hours and minutes are used in scientific, as well as everyday, measurement of time. The only prefixes generally used are those indicating *fractional portions* of seconds—for example, millisecond and microsecond.

$$\text{microunit} \underset{\times 1000}{\overset{\div 1000}{\rightleftharpoons}} \text{milliunit} \underset{\times 10}{\overset{\div 10}{\rightleftharpoons}} \text{centiunit} \underset{\times 100}{\overset{\div 100}{\rightleftharpoons}} \text{unit} \underset{\times 1000}{\overset{\div 1000}{\rightleftharpoons}} \text{kilounit}$$

smallest ⇌ largest

The objectives of the sections that follow are to provide a brief overview of the most-used measurements in science or health professions and to help you gain some measure of confidence in dealing with them. (A listing of the most frequently used conversion factors, for conversions between British and metric system units, is provided in Appendix A.)

Length Measurements

The metric unit of length is the **meter (m).** Smaller objects are measured in centimeters or millimeters. Subcellular structures are measured in micrometers.

To help you picture these units of length, some equivalents follow:

One meter (m) is slightly longer than one yard (1 m = 39.37 in.).

One centimeter (cm) is approximately the width of a piece of chalk. (Note: There are 2.54 cm in 1 in.)

One millimeter (mm) is approximately the thickness of the wire of a paper clip or of a mark made by a No. 2 pencil lead.

One micrometer (µm) is extremely tiny and can be measured only microscopically.

Make the following conversions between metric units of length:

9. 12 cm = _____ mm

10. 2000 µm = _____ mm

Now, circle the answer that would make the most sense in each of the following statements:

11. A match (in a matchbook) is (0.3, 3, 30) cm long.

12. A standard-size American car is about 4 (mm, cm, m, km) long.

Volume Measurements

The metric unit of volume is the liter. A **liter** (l, or sometimes L, especially without a prefix) is slightly more than a quart (1 L = 1.057 quarts). Liquid volumes measured out for lab experiments are usually measured in milliliters (ml). (The terms *ml* and *cc*, cubic centimeter, are used interchangeably in laboratory and medical settings.)

To help you visualize metric volumes, the equivalents of some common substances follow:

A 12-oz can of soda is a little less than 360 ml.

A fluid ounce is about 30 (it's 29.57) ml (cc).

A teaspoon of vanilla is about 5 ml (cc).

Compute the following:

13. How many 5-ml injections can be prepared from 1 liter of a medicine? _____

14. A 450-ml volume of alcohol is _____ L.

Mass Measurements

Although many people use the terms *mass* and *weight* interchangeably, this usage is inaccurate. **Mass** is the amount of matter in an object; and an object has a constant mass, regardless of where it is—that is, on earth, or in outer space. However, weight varies with gravitational pull; the greater the gravitational pull, the greater the weight. Thus, our astronauts are said to be weightless* when in outer space, but they still have the same mass as they do on earth.

The metric unit of mass is the **gram (g).** Medical dosages are usually prescribed in milligrams (mg) or micrograms (µg); and in the clinical agency, body weight (particularly of infants) is typically specified in kilograms (kg) (1 kg = 2.2 lb).

The following examples are provided to help you become familiar with the masses of some common objects:

Two aspirin tablets have a mass of approximately 1 g.

A nickel has a mass of 5 g.

The mass of an average woman (132 lb) is 60 kg.

Make the following conversions:

15. 300 g = _____ mg = _____ µg

16. 4000 µg = _____ mg = _____ g

17. A nurse must administer to her patient, Mrs. Smith, 5 mg of a drug per kg of body mass. Mrs. Smith weighs 140 lb. How many grams of the drug should the nurse administer to her patient?

_____ g

Temperature Measurements

In the laboratory and in the clinical agency, temperature is measured both in metric units (degrees Celsius, °C) and in British units (degrees Fahrenheit, °F). Thus it helps to be familiar with both temperature scales.

The temperatures of boiling and freezing water can be used to compare the two scales:

The freezing point of water is 0°C and 32°F.

The boiling point of water is 100°C and 212°F.

---

* Astronauts are not *really* weightless. It is just that they and their surroundings are being pulled toward the earth at the same speed; and so, in reference to their environment, they appear to float.

As you can see, the range from the freezing point to the boiling point of water on the Celsius scale is 100 degrees, whereas the comparable range on the Fahrenheit scale is 180 degrees. Hence, one degree on the Celsius scale represents a greater change in temperature. Normal body temperature is approximately 98.6°F or 37°C.

To convert from the Celsius scale to the Fahrenheit scale, the following equation is used:

$$°C = \frac{5(°F - 32)}{9}$$

To convert from the Fahrenheit scale to the Celsius scale, the following equation is used:

$$°F = (9/5 \ °C) + 32$$

Perform the following temperature conversions:

18. Convert 38°C to °F: _____

19. Convert 158°F to °C: _____

Answers

1. range of 94–64 or 30 beats/min; mean 77.5

2. 3800%

3. 75%

4. 160%

5. 8

6. 0.0005

7. 10 breaths/min

8. interval between 100–102° (went from 22 to 36 breaths/min)

9. 12 cm = 120 mm

10. 2000 μm = 2 mm

11. 3 cm long

12. 4 m long

13. 200

14. 0.45 L

15. 300 g = 3 × 10^5 mg = 3 × 10^8 μg

16. 4000 μg = 4 mg = 4 × 10^{-3} g (0.004 g)

17. 0.32 g

18. 100.4°F

19. 70°C

Functional Anatomy of the Endocrine Glands

MATERIALS

- ☐ Human torso model
- ☐ Anatomical chart of the human endocrine system
- ☐ Compound microscope
- ☐ Prepared slides of the anterior pituitary,* posterior pituitary, thyroid gland, parathyroid glands, adrenal gland, and pancreas*

  ✂ For instructions on animal dissections, see the dissection exercises starting on page 697 in the cat, fetal pig, and rat editions of this manual.

*With differential staining if possible

OBJECTIVES

1. To identify and name the major endocrine glands and tissues of the body when provided with an appropriate diagram.
2. To list the hormones produced by the endocrine glands and discuss the general function of each.
3. To indicate the means by which hormones contribute to body homeostasis by giving appropriate examples of hormonal actions.
4. To cite mechanisms by which the endocrine glands are stimulated to release their hormones.
5. To describe the structural and functional relationship between the hypothalamus and the pituitary.
6. To describe a major pathological consequence of hypersecretion and hyposecretion of several of the hormones considered.
7. To correctly identify the histologic structure of the thyroid, parathyroid, pancreas, anterior and posterior pituitary, adrenal cortex, and adrenal medulla by microscopic inspection or when presented with an appropriate photomicrograph or diagram.
8. To name and point out the specialized hormone-secreting cells in the above tissues as studied in the laboratory.

PRE-LAB QUIZ

1. Define *hormone*. _____
2. Circle the correct term. An <u>endocrine / exocrine</u> gland is a ductless gland that empties its hormone into the extracellular fluid, from which it enters the blood.
3. The pituitary gland, also known as the _____, is located in the sella turcica of the sphenoid bone.
   a. hypophysis
   b. hypothalamus
   c. thalamus
4. Circle True or False. The anterior pituitary gland is also referred to as the master endocrine gland because it controls the activity of many other endocrine glands.
5. The _____ gland composed of two lobes, is located in the throat, just inferior to the larynx.
   a. pancreas   c. thymus
   b. posterior pituitary   d. thyroid
6. The pancreas produces two hormones that are responsible for regulating blood sugar levels. Name the hormone that increases blood glucose levels. _____
7. Circle True or False. The gonads are considered to be both endocrine and exocrine glands.

Text continues on next page.

myA&P *For practice quizzes on this lab, go to www.myaandp.com.*

PAL *For access to anatomical models and more, check out Practice Anatomy Lab.*

8. This gland is rather large in an infant, but begins to atrophy at puberty and is relatively inconspicuous by old age. It produces hormones that direct the maturation of T cells. It is the _____ gland.
   a. pineal
   b. testes
   c. thymus
   d. thyroid

9. Circle the correct term. Islets of <u>Pancreatic islets</u> / <u>Acinar cells</u> form the endocrine portion of the pancreas.

10. The outer cortex of the adrenal gland is divided into three zones (zonas). Which one produces aldosterone?
    a. zona fasciculata
    b. zona glomerulosa
    c. zona reticularis

The **endocrine system** is the second major control system of the body. Acting with the nervous system, it helps coordinate and integrate the activity of the body's cells. However, the nervous system employs electrochemical impulses to bring about rapid control, whereas the more slowly acting endocrine system employs chemical "messengers," or **hormones,** which are released into the blood to be transported throughout the body.

The term *hormone* comes from a Greek word meaning "to arouse." The body's hormones, which are steroids or amino acid–based molecules, arouse the body's tissues and cells by stimulating changes in their metabolic activity. These changes lead to growth and development and to the physiological homeostasis of many body systems. Although all hormones are bloodborne, a given hormone affects only the biochemical activity of a specific organ or organs. Organs that respond to a particular hormone are referred to as the **target organs** of that hormone. The ability of the target tissue to respond seems to depend on the ability of the hormone to bind with specific receptors (proteins) occurring on the cells' plasma membrane or within the cells.

Although the function of some hormone-producing glands (the anterior pituitary, thyroid, adrenals, parathyroids) is purely endocrine, the function of others (the pancreas and gonads) is mixed—both endocrine and exocrine. Both types of glands are derived from epithelium, but the endocrine, or ductless, glands release their product (always hormonal) directly into the extracellular fluid from which it enters blood or lymph. The exocrine glands release their products at the body's surface or upon an epithelial membrane via ducts. In addition, there are hormone-producing cells in the heart, the gastrointestinal tract, kidney, skin, adipose tissue, skeleton, and placenta, organs whose functions are primarily nonendocrine. Only the major endocrine organs, plus the pineal gland and the thymus, are considered here.

Gross Anatomy and Basic Function of the Endocrine Glands

Pituitary Gland (Hypophysis)

The *pituitary gland,* or *hypophysis,* is located in the hypophyseal fossa of the sella turcica of the sphenoid bone. It consists largely of two functional *lobes,* the **adenohypophysis,** or **anterior pituitary,** and the **neurohypophysis,** consisting mainly of the **posterior pituitary** (Figure 27.1). The pituitary gland is attached to the hypothalamus by a stalk called the **infundibulum.**

Anterior Pituitary Hormones

The anterior pituitary (lobe) secretes a number of hormones. Four of these are **tropic hormones.** A tropic hormone stimulates its target organ, which is also an endocrine gland, to secrete its hormones. Target organ hormones then exert their effects on other body organs and tissues. The anterior pituitary tropic hormones include:

• **Gonadotropins–follicle-stimulating hormone (FSH)** and **luteinizing hormone (LH)**—regulate gamete production and hormonal activity of the gonads (ovaries and testes). The precise roles of the gonadotropins are described in Exercise 43 along with other considerations of reproductive system physiology.

• **Adrenocorticotropic hormone (ACTH)** regulates the endocrine activity of the cortex portion of the adrenal gland.

• **Thyroid-stimulating hormone (TSH),** or **thyrotropin,** influences the growth and activity of the thyroid gland.

The two other important hormones produced by the anterior pituitary are not directly involved in the regulation of other endocrine glands of the body.

• **Growth hormone (GH)** is a general metabolic hormone that plays an important role in determining body size. It affects many tissues of the body; however, its major effects are exerted on the growth of muscle and the long bones of the body. Hyposecretion results in pituitary dwarfism in children. Hypersecretion causes gigantism in children and **acromegaly** (overgrowth of bones in hands, feet, and face) in adults. ■

• **Prolactin (PRL)** stimulates breast development and promotes and maintains lactation by the mammary glands after childbirth. It may stimulate testosterone production in males.

A less important secretory product of the anterior pituitary is pro-opiomelanocortin (POMC), a prohormone. POMC is split by enzymes into ACTH, enkephalin and beta endorphin (natural opiates), and melanocyte-stimulating hormone (MSH).

The anterior pituitary controls the activity of so many other endocrine glands that it has often been called the *master endocrine gland.* However, the anterior pituitary is controlled by neurosecretions, *releasing* or *inhibiting hormones,* produced by neurons of the ventral hypothalamus. These hypothalamic hormones are liberated into the **hypophyseal portal system** (Figure 27.1), and carried to cells of the anterior pituitary where they control release of anterior pituitary hormones.

Posterior Pituitary Hormones
The posterior pituitary (lobe) is not an endocrine gland in a strict sense because it

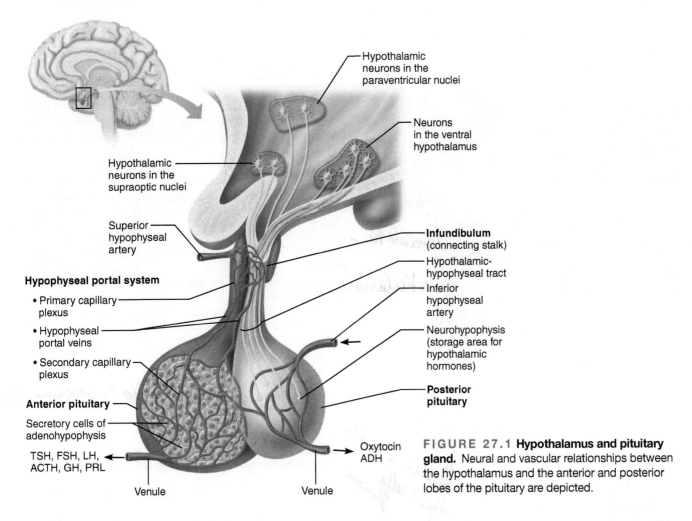

Labels in figure:

Hypothalamic neurons in the paraventricular nuclei

Neurons in the ventral hypothalamus

Hypothalamic neurons in the supraoptic nuclei

Superior hypophyseal artery

Infundibulum (connecting stalk)

Hypothalamic-hypophyseal tract

Inferior hypophyseal artery

Hypophyseal portal system
- Primary capillary plexus
- Hypophyseal portal veins
- Secondary capillary plexus

Neurohypophysis (storage area for hypothalamic hormones)

Anterior pituitary

Secretory cells of adenohypophysis

Posterior pituitary

TSH, FSH, LH, ACTH, GH, PRL

Venule

Venule

Oxytocin ADH

FIGURE 27.1 Hypothalamus and pituitary gland. Neural and vascular relationships between the hypothalamus and the anterior and posterior lobes of the pituitary are depicted.

does not synthesize the hormones it releases. Instead, it acts as a storage area for two hormones transported to it via the axons of neurons in the paraventricular and supraoptic nuclei of the hypothalamus. The hormones are released in response to nerve impulses from these neurons. The first of these hormones is **oxytocin,** which stimulates powerful uterine contractions during birth and coitus and also causes milk ejection in the lactating mother. The second, **antidiuretic hormone (ADH),** causes the distal and collecting tubules of the kidneys to reabsorb more water from the urinary filtrate, thereby reducing urine output and conserving body water.

Hyposecretion of ADH results in dehydration from excessive urine output, a condition called **diabetes insipidus.** Individuals with this condition experience an insatiable thirst. Hypersecretion results in edema, headache, and disorientation. ■

Pineal Gland

The *pineal gland* is a small cone-shaped gland located in the roof of the third ventricle of the brain. Its major endocrine product is **melatonin,** which exhibits a diurnal (daily) cycle. It peaks at night, making us drowsy, and is lowest around noon.

The endocrine role of the pineal body in humans is still controversial, but it is known to play a role in the biological rhythms (particularly mating and migratory behavior) of other animals. In humans, melatonin appears to exert some in-

hibitory effect on the reproductive system that prevents precocious sexual maturation.

Thyroid Gland

The *thyroid gland* is composed of two lobes joined by a central mass, or isthmus. It is located in the throat, just inferior to the larynx. It produces two major hormones, thyroid hormone and calcitonin.

Thyroid hormone (TH) is actually two physiologically active hormones known as T_4 **(thyroxine)** and T_3 **(triiodothyronine).** Because its primary function is to control the rate of body metabolism and cellular oxidation, TH affects virtually every cell in the body.

Hyposecretion of thyroxine leads to a condition of mental and physical sluggishness, which is called **myxedema** in the adult. Hypersecretion causes elevated metabolic rate, nervousness, weight loss, sweating, and irregular heartbeat. ■

Calcitonin decreases blood calcium levels by stimulating calcium salt deposit in the bones. Although it acts antagonistically to parathyroid hormone, the hormonal product of the parathyroid glands, calcitonin is not involved in day-to-day control of calcium homeostasis.

Parathyroid Glands

The *parathyroid glands* are found embedded in the posterior surface of the thyroid gland. Typically, there are two

[handwritten annotations: Anterior pituitary - granular / TSH thyroid / FSH gonad / ACTH adrenal / +1 adrenal cortex / Prolactin breast / colloid follicular cells / glomerulosa]

Adrenal Glands

The two *adrenal,* or *suprarenal, glands* are located atop or close to the kidneys. Anatomically, the **adrenal medulla** develops from neural crest tissue, and it is directly controlled by the sympathetic nervous system. The medullary cells respond to this stimulation by releasing **epinephrine** (80%) or **norepinephrine** (20%), which act in conjunction with the sympathetic nervous system to elicit the fight-or-flight response to stressors.

The **adrenal cortex** produces three major groups of steroid hormones, collectively called **corticosteroids.** The **mineralocorticoids,** chiefly *aldosterone,* regulate water and electrolyte balance in the extracellular fluids, mainly by regulating sodium ion reabsorption by kidney tubules. The **glucocorticoids** (*cortisol* [*hydrocortisone*], *cortisone,* and *corticosterone*) enable the body to resist long-term stressors, primarily by increasing blood glucose levels. The **gonadocorticoids,** or **sex hormones,** produced by the adrenal cortex are chiefly *androgens* (male sex hormones), but some *estrogens* (female sex hormones) are formed.

The gonadocorticoids are produced throughout life in relatively insignificant amounts; however, hypersecretion of these hormones produces abnormal hairiness (**hirsutism**), and masculinization occurs. ■

Pancreas

The *pancreas,* located partially behind the stomach in the abdomen, functions as both an endocrine and exocrine gland. It produces digestive enzymes as well as insulin and glucagon, important hormones concerned with the regulation of blood sugar levels.

Elevated blood glucose levels stimulate release of **insulin,** which decreases blood sugar levels, primarily by accelerating the transport of glucose into the body cells, where it is oxidized for energy or converted to glycogen or fat for storage.

Hyposecretion of insulin or some deficiency in the insulin receptors leads to **diabetes mellitus,** which is characterized by the inability of body cells to utilize glucose and the subsequent loss of glucose in the urine. Alterations of protein and fat metabolism also occur secondary to derangements in carbohydrate metabolism. Hypersecretion causes low blood sugar, or **hypoglycemia.** Symptoms include anxiety, nervousness, tremors, and weakness. ■

Glucagon acts antagonistically to insulin. When blood glucose levels are low, it stimulates the liver, its primary target organ, to break down glycogen stores to glucose and subsequently to release the glucose to the blood.

The Gonads

The *female gonads,* or *ovaries,* are paired, almond-sized organs located in the pelvic cavity. In addition to producing the female sex cells (ova), the ovaries produce two steroid hormone groups, the estrogens and progesterone. The endocrine and exocrine functions of the ovaries do not begin until the onset of puberty. The **estrogens** are responsible for the development of the secondary sex characteristics of the female at puberty (primarily maturation of the reproductive organs and development of the breasts) and act with progesterone to bring about cyclic changes of the uterine lining that occur during the menstrual cycle. The estrogens also help prepare the mammary glands for lactation. During pregnancy progesterone

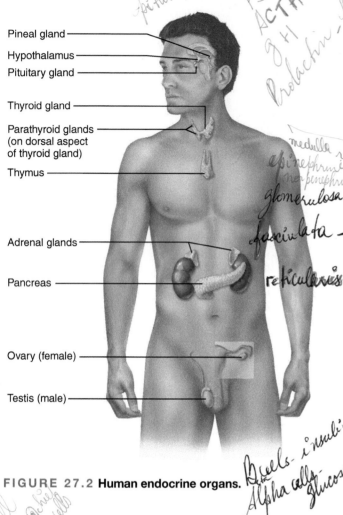

Pineal gland
Hypothalamus
Pituitary gland
Thyroid gland
Parathyroid glands (on dorsal aspect of thyroid gland)
Thymus
Adrenal glands
Pancreas
Ovary (female)
Testis (male)

FIGURE 27.2 Human endocrine organs.

[handwritten annotations: medulla epinephrine / norepinephrine / glomerulosa / fasciculata / reticularis / dual organ - endo & exocrine 98% / Beta cells - insulin / Alpha cells - glucose]

small oval glands on each lobe, but there may be more and some may be located in other regions of the neck. They secrete **parathyroid hormone (PTH),** the most important regulator of calcium balance of the blood. When blood calcium levels decrease below a certain critical level, the parathyroids release PTH, which causes release of calcium from bone matrix and prods the kidney to reabsorb more calcium and less phosphate from the filtrate. PTH also stimulates the kidneys to convert vitamin D to its active D_3 form, *calcitriol.*

Hyposecretion increases neural excitability and may lead to **tetany,** prolonged muscle spasms that can result in respiratory paralysis and death. Hypersecretion of PTH results in loss of calcium from bones, causing deformation, softening, and spontaneous fractures. ■

Thymus

[handwritten: part of lymphatic system]

The *thymus* is a bilobed gland situated in the superior thorax, posterior to the sternum and anterior to the heart and lungs. Conspicuous in the infant, it begins to atrophy at puberty, and by old age it is relatively inconspicuous. The thymus produces several different families of hormones including **thymulin, thymosins,** and **thymopoietins.** These hormones are thought to be involved in the development of T lymphocytes and the immune response. Their role is poorly understood; they appear to act mainly locally as paracrines.

[handwritten annotations at bottom: principal cell / chief cells / lymphocytes / Follicle / oocyte graafian follicle / Seminiferous tubule]

maintains the uterine musculature in a quiescent state and helps to prepare the breast tissue for lactation.

The paired oval *testes* of the male are suspended in a pouchlike sac, the scrotum, outside the pelvic cavity. In addition to the male sex cells (sperm), the testes produce the male sex hormone, **testosterone.** Testosterone promotes the maturation of the reproductive system accessory structures, brings about the development of the male secondary sex characteristics, and is responsible for sexual drive, or libido. Both the endocrine and exocrine functions of the testes begin at puberty. For a more detailed discussion of the function and histology of the ovaries and testes, see Exercises 42 and 43.

ACTIVITY 1

Identifying the Endocrine Organs

Locate the endocrine organs on Figure 27.2. Also locate these organs on the anatomical charts or torso. ■

Microscopic Anatomy of Selected Endocrine Glands

ACTIVITY 2

Examining the Microscopic Structure of Endocrine Glands

Obtain a microscope and one of each slide on the materials list. We will study only organs in which it is possible to identify the endocrine-producing cells. Compare your observations with the histology images in Figure 27.3a–f.

Thyroid Gland

1. Scan the thyroid under low power, noting the **follicles,** spherical sacs containing a pink-stained material *(colloid).* Stored T_3 and T_4 are attached to the protein colloidal material stored in the follicles as **thyroglobulin** and are released gradually to the blood. Compare the tissue viewed to Figure 27.3a.

2. Observe the tissue under high power. Notice that the walls of the follicles are formed by simple cuboidal or squamous epithelial cells that synthesize the follicular products. The **parafollicular,** or **C, cells** you see between the follicles are responsible for calcitonin production.

When the thyroid gland is actively secreting, the follicles appear small, and the colloidal material has a ruffled border. When the thyroid is hypoactive or inactive, the follicles are large and plump, and the follicular epithelium appears to be squamouslike.

Parathyroid Glands

Observe the parathyroid tissue under low power to view its two major cell types, the chief cells and the oxyphil cells. Compare your observations to Figure 27.3b. The **chief cells,** which synthesize parathyroid hormone (PTH), are small and abundant, and arranged in thick branching cords. The function of the scattered, much larger **oxyphil cells** is unknown.

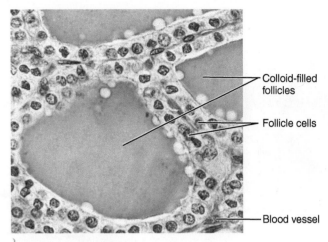

(a) Thyroid gland (330×)

Colloid-filled follicles

Follicle cells

Blood vessel

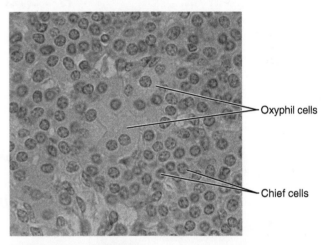

(b) Parathyroid gland (330×)

Oxyphil cells

Chief cells

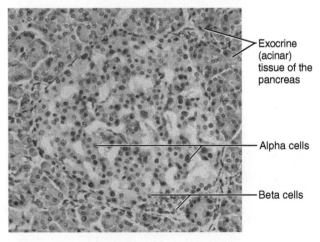

(c) Pancreatic islet (170×)

Exocrine (acinar) tissue of the pancreas

Alpha cells

Beta cells

FIGURE 27.3 Microscopic anatomy of selected endocrine organs.

Pancreas

1. Observe pancreas tissue under low power to identify the roughly circular **pancreatic islets (islets of Langerhans),** the endocrine portions of the pancreas. The islets are scattered

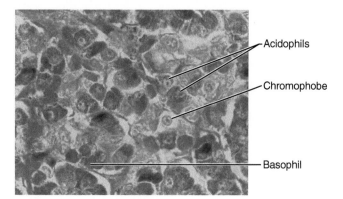

(d) Anterior pituitary (280×)

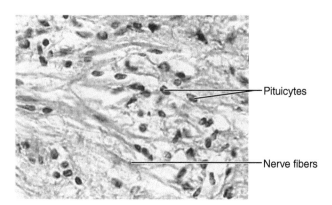

(e) Posterior pituitary (465×)

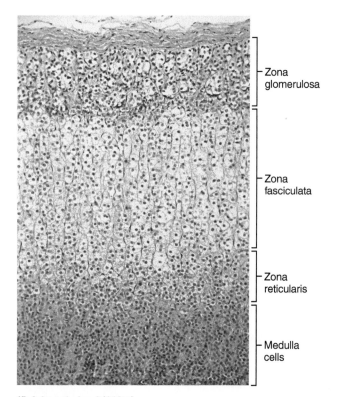

(f) Adrenal gland (110×)

FIGURE 27.3 *(continued)* **Microscopic anatomy of selected endocrine organs.**

amid the more numerous **acinar cells** and stain differently (usually lighter), which makes their identification possible. The deeper-staining acinar cells form the major portion of the pancreatic tissue. Acinar cells produce the exocrine secretion of hydrolytic enzymes that is released into the duodenum through the pancreatic duct. Alkaline fluid produced by duct cells accompanies the hydrolytic enzymes. See Figure 27.3c.

2. Focus on islet cells under high power. Notice that they are densely packed and have no definite arrangement. In contrast, the cuboidal acinar cells are arranged around secretory ducts. If special stains are used, it will be possible to distinguish the **alpha cells,** which tend to cluster at the periphery of the islets and produce glucagon, from the **beta cells,** which synthesize insulin. With these specific stains, the beta cells are larger and stain gray-blue, and the alpha cells are smaller and appear bright pink, as shown in Figure 27.3c.

Pituitary Gland

1. Observe the general structure of the pituitary gland under low power to differentiate between the glandular anterior pituitary and the neural posterior pituitary.

2. Using the high-power lens, focus on the nests of cells of the anterior pituitary. When differential stains are used it is possible to identify the specialized cell types that secrete the specific hormones. Using the photomicrograph in Figure 27.3d as a guide, locate the reddish brown–stained **acidophil cells,** which produce growth hormone and prolactin, and the **basophil cells,** whose deep-blue granules are responsible for the production of the tropic hormones (TSH, ACTH, FSH, and LH). **Chromophobes,** the third cellular population, do not take up the stain and appear rather dull and colorless. The role of the chromophobes is controversial, but they apparently are not directly involved in hormone production.

3. Switch your focus to the posterior pituitary where two hormones (oxytocin and antidiuretic hormone) synthesized by hypothalamic neurons are stored. Observe the axons of hypothalamic neurons that compose most of this portion of the pituitary. Also note the glial cells, or **pituicytes** (Figure 27.3e).

Adrenal Gland

1. Hold the slide of the adrenal gland up to the light to distinguish the outer cortex and inner medulla areas. Then scan the cortex under low power to distinguish the differences in cell appearance and arrangement in the three cortical areas. Refer to Figure 27.3f as you work. In the outermost **zona glomerulosa,** where most mineralocorticoid production occurs, the tightly packed cells are arranged in spherical clusters. The deeper intermediate **zona fasciculata** produces glucocorticoids. This is the thickest part of the cortex. Its cells are arranged in parallel cords. The innermost cortical zone, the **zona reticularis** produces sex hormones and some glucocorticoids. The cells here stain intensely and form a branching network.

2. Switch to higher power to view the large, lightly stained cells of the adrenal medulla, which produce epinephrine and norepinephrine. Notice their clumped arrangement. ■■■

NAME _____

LAB TIME/DATE _____

Functional Anatomy of the Endocrine Glands

Gross Anatomy and Basic Function of the Endocrine Glands

1. Both the endocrine and nervous systems are major regulating systems of the body; however, the nervous system has been compared to an airmail delivery system and the endocrine system to the Pony Express. Briefly explain this comparison.

_____

_____

_____

2. Define *hormone.* _____

_____

3. Chemically, hormones belong chiefly to two molecular groups, the _____

and the _____.

4. Define *target organ.* _____

_____

5. If hormones travel in the bloodstream, why don't all tissues respond to all hormones? _____

_____

6. Identify the endocrine organ described by each of the following statements.

_____ 1. located in the throat; bilobed gland connected by an isthmus

_____ 2. found close to the kidney

_____ 3. a mixed gland, located close to the stomach and small intestine

_____ 4. paired glands suspended in the scrotum

_____ 5. ride "horseback" on the thyroid gland

_____ 6. found in the pelvic cavity of the female, concerned with ova and female hormone production

_____ 7. found in the upper thorax overlying the heart; large during youth

_____ 8. found in the roof of the third ventricle

7. The table below lists the functions of many of the hormones you have studied. From the keys below, fill in the hormones responsible for each function, and the endocrine glands that produce each hormone. Glands may be used more than once.

Hormones Key:

ACTH	estrogens	progesterone
ADH	FSH	prolactin
aldosterone	glucagon	PTH
calcitonin	insulin	T_3/T_4
cortisol	LH	testosterone
epinephrine	oxytocin	TSH

Glands Key:

adrenal cortex	pancreas
adrenal medulla	parathyroid glands
anterior pituitary	posterior pituitary
hypothalamus	testes
ovaries	thyroid gland

Function	Hormone(s)	Gland(s)
Regulate the function of another endocrine gland	1.	
	2.	
	3.	
	4.	
Maintenance of salt and water balance in the extracellular fluid	1.	
	2.	
Directly involved in milk production and ejection	1.	
	2.	
Controls the rate of body metabolism and cellular oxidation	1.	
Regulate blood calcium levels	1.	
	2.	
Regulate blood glucose levels; produced by the same "mixed" gland	1.	
	2.	
Released in response to stressors	1.	
	2.	
Drive development of secondary sex characteristics in males	1.	
Directly responsible for regulation of the menstrual cycle	1.	
	2.	

8. Although the pituitary gland is often referred to as the master gland of the body, the hypothalamus exerts some control over the pituitary gland. How does the hypothalamus control both anterior and posterior pituitary functioning?

_____

_____

9. Indicate whether the release of the hormones listed below is stimulated by (A) another hormone; (B) the nervous system (neurotransmitters, or neurosecretions); or (C) humoral factors (the concentration of specific nonhormonal substances in the blood or extracellular fluid). (Use your textbook as necessary.)

_____ 1. ACTH   _____ 4. insulin   _____ 7. T_4/T_3

_____ 2. calcitonin   _____ 5. norepinephrine   _____ 8. testosterone

_____ 3. estrogens   _____ 6. parathyroid hormone   _____ 9. TSH, FSH

10. Name the hormone(s) produced in *inadequate* amounts that directly result in the following conditions.

_____ 1. tetany

_____ 2. excessive diuresis without high blood glucose levels

_____ 3. loss of glucose in the urine

_____ 4. abnormally small stature, normal proportions

_____ 5. low BMR, mental and physical sluggishness

11. Name the hormone(s) produced in *excessive* amounts that directly result in the following conditions.

_____ 1. large hands and feet in the adult, large facial bones

_____ 2. nervousness, irregular pulse rate, sweating

_____ 3. demineralization of bones, spontaneous fractures

Microscopic Anatomy of Selected Endocrine Glands

12. Choose a response from the key below to name the hormone(s) produced by the cell types listed.

Key: a. *calcitonin*   d. glucocorticoids   g. PTH
      b. GH, prolactin   e. insulin   h. T_4/T_3
      c. glucagon   f. mineralocorticoids   i. TSH, ACTH, FSH, LH

_____ 1. parafollicular cells of the thyroid   _____ 6. zona fasciculata cells

_____ 2. follicular epithelial cells of the thyroid   _____ 7. zona glomerulosa cells

_____ 3. beta cells of the pancreatic islets (islets _____ 8. chief cells of the parathyroid
            of Langerhans)
                                                         _____ 9. acidophil cells of the anterior pituitary
_____ 4. alpha cells of the pancreatic islets (islets
            of Langerhans)

_____ 5. basophil cells of the anterior pituitary

13. Six diagrams of the microscopic structures of the endocrine glands are presented here. Identify each and name all structures indicated by a leader line or bracket.

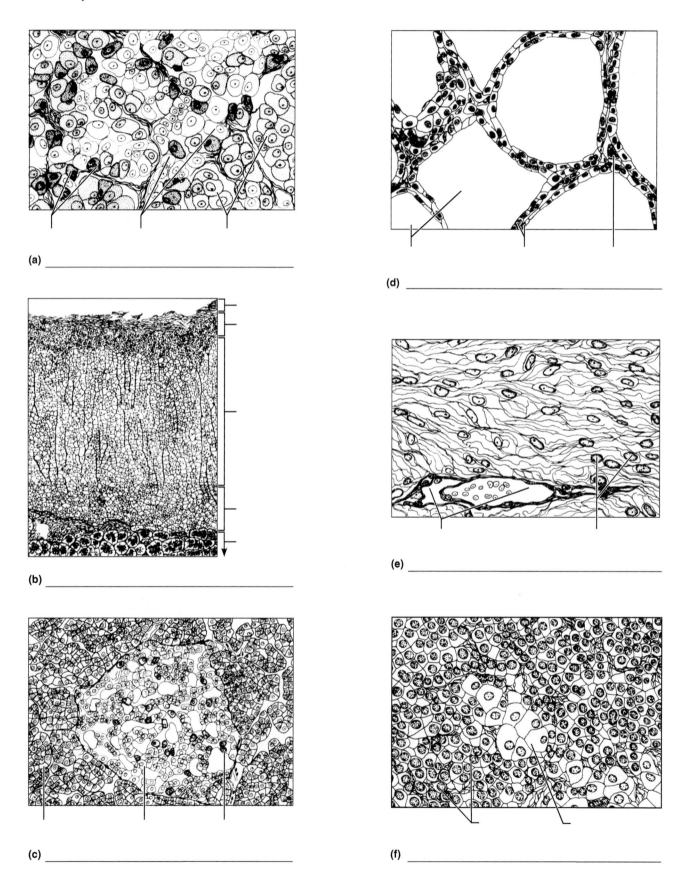

(a) _____

(b) _____

(c) _____

(d) _____

(e) _____

(f) _____

Role of Thyroid Hormone, Pituitary Hormone, Insulin, and Epinephrine: Wet Lab

M A T E R I A L S

Activity 1: Thyroid hormone and metabolic rate

☐ Glass desiccator, manometer, 20-ml glass syringe, two-hole rubber stopper, and T-valve (1 for every 3–4 students)

☐ Soda lime (desiccant)

☐ Hardware cloth squares

☐ Petrolatum

☐ Rubber tubing; tubing clamp; scissors

☐ 7.6-cm (3-in.) pieces of glass tubing

☐ Animal balances

☐ Heavy animal-handling gloves

☐ Young rats of the same sex, obtained 2 weeks prior to the laboratory session and treated as follows for 14 days:

Group 1: control group—fed normal rat chow and water

Group 2: experimental group A—fed normal rat chow and drinking water containing 0.02% propylthiouracil*

Group 3: experimental group B—fed rat chow containing desiccated thyroid (2% by weight) and given normal drinking water

☐ Chart set up on chalkboard so that each student group can record its computed metabolic rate figures under the appropriate headings

*__Note to the Instructor:__ propylthiouracil (PTU) is degraded by light and should be stored in light-resistant containers or in the dark.

Text continues on next page.

O B J E C T I V E S

1. To understand the physiological (and clinical) importance of metabolic rate measurement.
2. To investigate the effect of hypo-, hyper-, and euthyroid conditions on oxygen consumption and metabolic rate.
3. To assemble the necessary apparatus and properly use a manometer to obtain experimental results.
4. To calculate metabolic rate in terms of O_2 consumption.
5. To describe and explain the effect of pituitary hormones on the ovary.
6. To describe and explain the effects of hyperinsulinism.
7. To describe and explain the effect of epinephrine on the heart.

P R E - L A B   Q U I Z

1. Define *metabolism.* _____
   _____
2. Circle the correct term. <u>Catabolism / Anabolism</u> is the process by which substances are broken down into simpler substances.
3. _____ is the single most important hormone responsible for influencing the rate of cellular metabolism and body heat production.
   a. Calcitonin   c. Insulin
   b. Estrogen   d. Thyroid hormone
4. Circle the correct term. <u>Control / Experimental group B</u> animals are assumed to have normal thyroid function and metabolic rate.
5. Basal metabolic rate (BMR) is:
   a. decreased in individuals with hyperthyroidism
   b. increased in individuals with hyperthyroidism
   c. increased in obese individuals
6. In this activity, _____ consumption will be measured with a respirator-manometer device.
   a. carbon dioxide   c. oxygen
   b. food   d. water
7. Circle True or False. Gonadotropins are produced by the anterior pituitary gland.
8. Circle the correct term. Many people with diabetes mellitus need injections of <u>insulin / glucagon</u> to maintain homeostasis.
9. What experiment will you do to observe the effects of epinephrine?
   a. Flush the heart of a dissected frog with epinephrine.
   b. Flush the heart of a dissected frog with insulin.
   c. Inject a rat with epinephrine.
   d. Inject a rat with follicle-stimulating hormone and epinephrine.

myA&P *For practice quizzes on this lab, go to www.myaandp.com.*

Activity 2: Pituitary hormone and ovary†

☐ Female frogs (*Rana pipiens*)

☐ Disposable gloves

☐ Battery jars

☐ Syringe (2-ml capacity)

☐ 20- to 25-gauge needle

☐ Frog pituitary extract

☐ Physiological saline

☐ Spring or pond water

☐ Wax marking pencils

Activity 3: Hyperinsulinism†

☐ 500- or 600-ml beakers

☐ 20% glucose solution

☐ Commercial insulin solution (400 Immunizing units [IU] per 100 ml of H_2O)

☐ Finger bowls

☐ Small (4–5 cm, or 1½–2 in.) freshwater fish (guppy, bluegill, or sunfish—listed in order of preference)

☐ Wax marking pencils

Activity 4: Epinephrine and heart†

☐ Frog (*Rana pipiens*)

☐ Dissecting instruments, tray, and pins

☐ Frog Ringer's solution in dropper bottle

☐ 1:1000 epinephrine (Adrenalin) solution in dropper bottles

☐ Disposable gloves

PEx PhysioEx™ 8.0 Computer Simulation on page PEx-49

†*The Selected Actions of Hormones and Other Chemical Messengers* videotape (available to qualified adopters from Pearson Education) may be used in lieu of student participation in Activities 2–4 of Exercise 28A.

The endocrine system exerts many complex and interrelated effects on the body as a whole, as well as on specific organs and tissues. Most scientific knowledge about this system is contemporary, and new information is constantly being presented. Many experiments on the endocrine system require relatively large laboratory animals; are time-consuming (requiring days to weeks of observation); and often involve technically difficult surgical procedures to remove the glands or parts of them, all of which makes it difficult to conduct more general types of laboratory experiments. Nevertheless, the four technically unsophisticated experiments presented here should illustrate how dramatically hormones affect body functioning.

To conserve laboratory specimens, experiments can be conducted by groups of four students. The use of larger working groups should not detract from benefits gained, since the major value of these experiments lies in observation.

ACTIVITY 1

Determining the Effect of Thyroid Hormone on Metabolic Rate

Metabolism is a broad term referring to all chemical reactions that are necessary to maintain life. It involves both *catabolism,* enzymatically controlled processes in which substances are broken down to simpler substances, and *anabolism,* processes in which larger molecules or structures are built from smaller ones. Most catabolic reactions in the body are accompanied by a net release of energy. Some of the liberated energy is captured to make ATP, the energy-rich molecule used by body cells to energize all their activities; the balance is lost in the form of thermal energy or heat. Maintaining body temperature is critically related to the heat-liberating aspects of metabolism.

Various foodstuffs make different contributions to the process of metabolism. For example, carbohydrates, particularly glucose, are generally broken down or oxidized to make ATP, whereas fats are utilized to form cell membranes and myelin sheaths, and to insulate the body with a fatty cushion. Fats are used secondarily for producing ATP, particularly when the diet is inadequate in carbohydrates. Proteins and amino acids tend to be conserved by body cells, and understandably so, since most structural elements of the body are proteinaceous in nature.

Thyroid hormone (collectively T_3 and T_4), produced by the thyroid gland, is the single most important hormone influencing the rate of cellular metabolism and body heat production.

Under conditions of excess thyroid hormone production (hyperthyroidism), an individual's basal metabolic rate (BMR), heat production, and oxygen consumption increase, and the individual tends to lose weight and become heat-intolerant and irritable. Conversely, hypothyroid individuals become mentally and physically sluggish and obese, and are cold-intolerant because of their low BMR. ■

Many factors other than thyroid hormone levels contribute to metabolic rate (for example, body size and weight, age, and activity level), but the focus of the following experiment is to investigate how differences in thyroid hormone concentration affect metabolism.

Three groups of laboratory rats will be used. *Control group* animals are assumed to have normal thyroid function (to be euthyroid) and to have normal metabolic rates for their relative body weights. *Experimental group A* animals have received water containing the chemical propylthiouracil, which counteracts or antagonizes the effects of thyroid hormone in the body. *Experimental group B* animals have been fed rat chow containing dried thyroid tissue, which contains thyroid hormone. The rates of oxygen consumption (an indirect means of determining metabolic rate) in the animals of the three groups will be measured and compared to investigate the effects of hyperthyroid, hypothyroid, and euthyroid conditions.

Oxygen consumption will be measured with a simple respirometer-manometer apparatus. Each animal will be placed in a closed chamber containing soda lime. As carbon dioxide is evolved and expired, it will be absorbed by the soda lime; therefore, the pressure changes observed will indicate the volume of oxygen consumed by the animal during the testing interval. Students will work in groups of three to four to assemble the apparatus, make preliminary weight measurements on the animals, and record the data.

Preparing the Respirometer-Manometer Apparatus

1. Obtain a desiccator, a two-hole rubber stopper, a 20-ml glass syringe, a hardware cloth square, a T-valve, scissors, rubber tubing, two short pieces of glass tubing, soda lime, a manometer, a clamp, and petrolatum, and bring them to your laboratory bench. The apparatus will be assembled as illustrated in Figure 28A.1.

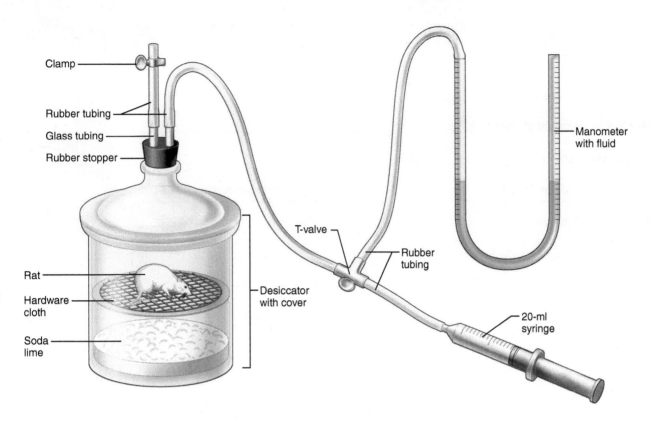

FIGURE 28A.1 Respirometer-manometer apparatus.

2. Shake soda lime into the bottom of the desiccator to thoroughly cover the glass bottom. Then place the hardware cloth on the ledge of the desiccator over the soda lime. The hardware cloth should be well above the soda lime, so that the animal will not be able to touch it. Soda lime is quite caustic and can cause chemical burns.

3. Lubricate the ends of the two pieces of glass tubing with petrolatum, and twist them into the holes in the rubber stopper until their distal ends protrude from the opposite side. *Do not plug the tubing with petrolatum.* Place the stopper into the desiccator cover, and set the cover on the desiccator temporarily.

4. Cut off a short (7.6-cm, or 3-in.) piece of rubber tubing, and attach it to the top of one piece of glass tubing extending from the stopper. Cut and attach a 30- to 35-cm (12- to 14-in.) piece of rubber tubing to the other glass tubing. Insert the T-valve stem into the distal end of the longer-length tubing.

5. Cut another short piece of rubber tubing; attach one end to the T-valve and the other to the nib of the 20-ml syringe. Remove the plunger of the syringe and grease its sides generously with petrolatum. Insert the plunger back into the syringe barrel and work it up and down to evenly disperse the petrolatum on the inner walls of the syringe, then pull the plunger out to the 20-ml marking.

6. Cut a piece of rubber tubing long enough to reach from the third arm of the T-valve to one arm of the manometer. (The manometer should be partially filled with water so that a U-shaped water column is seen.) Attach the tubing to the T-valve and the manometer arm.

7. Remove the desiccator cover and generously grease the cover's bottom edge with petrolatum. Place the cover back on

the desiccator and firmly move it from side to side to spread the lubricant evenly.

8. Test the system for leaks as follows: Firmly clamp the *short* length of rubber tubing extending from the stopper. Now gently push in on the plunger of the syringe. If the system is properly sealed, the fluid in the manometer will move away from the rubber tubing attached to its arm. If there is an air leak, the manometer fluid level will not change, or it will change and then quickly return to its original level. If either of these events occurs, check all glass-to-glass or glass-to-rubber tubing connections. Smear additional petrolatum on suspect areas and test again. The apparatus must be airtight before experimentation can begin.

9. After ensuring that there are no leaks in the system, unclamp the short rubber tubing, and remove the desiccator cover.

Preparing the Animal

⚠ 1. Put on the heavy animal-handling gloves, and obtain one of the animals as directed by your instructor. Handling it gently, weigh the animal to the nearest 0.1 g on the animal balance.

2. Carefully place the animal on the hardware cloth in the desiccator. The objective is to measure oxygen usage at basal levels, so you do not want to prod the rat into high levels of activity, which would produce errors in your measurements.

3. Record the animal's group (control or experimental group A or B) and its weight in kilograms (that is, weight in grams/1000) on the data sheet on page 418.

Metabolic Rate Data Sheet

Animal used from group: _____

14-day prior treatment of animal: _____

Body weight in grams: _____/1000 = body weight in kg: _____

O$_2$ consumption/min: Test 1 | **O$_2$ consumption/min: Test 2**

Beginning syringe reading _____ ml   Beginning syringe reading _____ ml

min 1 _____	min 6 _____	min 1 _____	min 6 _____
min 2 _____	min 7 _____	min 2 _____	min 7 _____
min 3 _____	min 8 _____	min 3 _____	min 8 _____
min 4 _____	min 9 _____	min 4 _____	min 9 _____
min 5 _____	min 10 _____	min 5 _____	min 10 _____

_____ Total O$_2$/10 min   _____ Total O$_2$/10 min

Average ml O$_2$ consumed/10 min: _____

Milliliters O$_2$ consumed/hr: _____

Metabolic rate: _____ ml O$_2$/kg/hr

Averaged class results:

Metabolic rate of control animals: _____ ml O$_2$/kg/hr

Metabolic rate of experimental group A animals (PTU-treated): _____ ml O$_2$/kg/hr

Metabolic rate of experimental group B animals (desiccated thyroid-treated): _____ ml O$_2$/kg/hr

---

Equilibrating the Chamber

1. Place the lid on the desiccator, and move it slightly from side to side to seal it firmly.

2. Leave the short tubing unclamped for 7 to 10 minutes to allow temperature equilibration in the chamber. (Since the animal's body heat will warm the air in the container, the air will expand initially. This must be allowed to occur before any measurements of oxygen consumption are taken. Otherwise, it would appear that the animal is generating oxygen rather than consuming it.)

Determining Oxygen Consumption of the Animal

1. Once again clamp the short rubber tubing extending from the desiccator lid stopper.

2. Check the manometer to make sure that the fluid level is the same in both arms. (If not, manipulate the syringe plunger

to make the fluid levels even.) Record the time and the position of the bottom of the plunger (use ml marking) in the syringe.

3. Observe the manometer fluid levels at 1-minute intervals. Each time make the necessary adjustment to bring the fluid levels even in the manometer by carefully pushing the syringe plunger further into the barrel. Determine the amount of oxygen used per minute in each interval by computing the difference in air volumes within the syringe. For example, if after the first minute, you push the plunger from the 20- to the 17-ml marking, the oxygen consumption would be 3 ml/min. Then, if the plunger is pushed from 17 ml to 15 ml at the second minute reading, the oxygen usage during minute 2 would be 2 ml, and so on.

4. Continue taking readings (and recording oxygen consumption per minute interval on the data sheet) for 10 consecutive minutes or until the syringe plunger has been pushed nearly to the 0-ml mark. Then unclamp the short rubber

tubing, remove the desiccator cover, and allow the apparatus to stand open for 2 to 3 minutes to flush out the stale air.

5. Repeat the recording procedures for another 10-minute interval. *Make sure that you equilibrate the temperature within the chamber before beginning this second recording series.*

6. After you have recorded the animal's oxygen consumption for two 10-minute intervals, unclamp the short rubber tubing, remove the desiccator lid, and carefully return the rat to its cage.

Computing Metabolic Rate

Metabolic rate calculations are generally reported in terms of kcal/m²/hr and require that corrections be made to present the data in terms of standardized pressure and temperature conditions. These more complex calculations will not be used here, since the object is simply to arrive at some generalized conclusions concerning the effect of thyroid hormone on metabolic rate.

1. Obtain the average figure for milliliters of oxygen consumed per 10-minute interval by adding up the minute-interval consumption figures for each 10-minute testing series and dividing the total by 2.

$$\frac{\text{Total ml O}_2 \text{ in test series 1} + \text{total ml O}_2 \text{ in test series 2}}{2}$$

2. Determine oxygen consumption per hour using the following formula, and record the figure on the data sheet:

$$\frac{\text{Average ml O}_2 \text{ consumed}}{10 \text{ min}} \times \frac{60 \text{ min}}{\text{hr}} = \text{ml O}_2/\text{hr}$$

3. To determine the metabolic rate in milliliters of oxygen consumed per kilogram of body weight per hour so that the results of all experiments can be compared, divide the figure just obtained in step 2 by the animal's weight in kilograms (kg = lb ÷ 2.2).

$$\text{Metabolic rate} = \frac{\text{ml O}_2/\text{hr}}{\text{weight (kg)}} = \underline{\qquad} \text{ ml O}_2/\text{kg/hr}$$

Record the metabolic rate on the data sheet and also in the appropriate space on the chart on the chalkboard.

4. Once all groups have recorded their final metabolic rate figures on the chalkboard, average the results of each animal grouping to obtain the mean for each experimental group. Also record this information on the data sheet. ■

ACTIVITY 2

Determining the Effect of Pituitary Hormones on the Ovary

As indicated in Exercise 43, anterior pituitary hormones called *gonadotropins,* specifically follicle-stimulating hormone (FSH) and luteinizing hormone (LH), regulate the ovarian cycles of the female. Although amphibians normally ovulate seasonally, many can be stimulated to ovulate "on demand" by injecting an extract of pituitary hormones.

1. Don disposable gloves, and obtain two frogs. Place them in separate battery jars to bring them to your laboratory bench. Also bring back a syringe and needle,

a wax marking pencil, pond or spring water, and containers of pituitary extract and physiological saline.

2. Before beginning, examine each frog for the presence of eggs. Hold the frog firmly with one hand and exert pressure on its abdomen toward the cloaca (in the direction of the legs). If ovulation has occurred, any eggs present in the oviduct will be forced out and will appear at the cloacal opening. If no eggs are present, continue with step 3.

If eggs are expressed, return the animal to your instructor and obtain another frog for experimentation. Repeat the procedure for determining if eggs are present until two frogs that lack eggs have been obtained.

3. Aspirate 1 to 2 ml of the pituitary extract into a syringe. Inject the extract subcutaneously into the anterior abdominal (peritoneal) cavity of the frog you have selected to be the experimental animal. To inject into the peritoneal cavity, hold the frog with its ventral surface superiorly. Insert the needle through the skin and muscles of the abdominal wall in the lower quarter of the abdomen. Do not insert the needle far enough to damage any of the vital organs. With a wax marker, label its large battery jar "experimental," and place the frog in it. Add a small amount of pond water to the battery jar before continuing.

4. Aspirate 1 to 2 ml of physiological saline into a syringe and inject it into the peritoneal cavity of the second frog—this will be the control animal. (Make sure you inject the same volume of fluid into both frogs.) Place this frog into the second battery jar, marked "control." Allow the animals to remain undisturbed for 24 hours.

5. After 24 hours,* again check each frog for the presence of eggs in the cloaca. (See step 2.) If no eggs are present, make arrangements with your laboratory instructor to return to the lab on the next day (at 48 hours after injection) to check your frogs for the presence of eggs.

6. Return the frogs to the terrarium before leaving or continuing with the lab.

In which of the prepared frogs was ovulation induced?

_____

Specifically, what hormone in the pituitary extract causes ovulation to occur?

_____ ■

ACTIVITY 3

Observing the Effects of Hyperinsulinism

Many people with diabetes mellitus need injections of insulin to maintain blood sugar (glucose) homeostasis. Adequate levels of blood glucose are essential for proper functioning of the nervous system; thus, the administration of insulin must be carefully controlled. If blood glucose levels fall precipitously, the patient will go into insulin shock.

*The student needs to inject the frog the day before the lab session or return to check results the day after the scheduled lab session.

A small fish will be used to demonstrate the effects of hyperinsulinism. Since the action of insulin on the fish parallels that in the human, this experiment should provide valid information concerning its administration to humans.

1. Prepare two finger bowls. Using a wax marking pencil, mark one A and the other B. To finger bowl A, add 100 ml of the commercial insulin solution. To finger bowl B, add 200 ml of 20% glucose solution.

2. Place a small fish in finger bowl A and observe its actions carefully as the insulin diffuses into its bloodstream through the capillary circulation of its gills.

Approximately how long did it take for the fish to become comatose?

_____

What types of activity did you observe in the fish before it became comatose?

_____

_____

_____

_____

3. When the fish is comatose, carefully transfer it to finger bowl B and observe its actions. What happens to the fish after it is transferred?

_____

_____

_____

_____

Approximately how long did it take for this recovery?

_____

4. After all observations have been made and recorded, carefully return the fish to the aquarium. ▪▪

ACTIVITY 4

Testing the Effect of Epinephrine on the Heart

As noted in Exercise 27, the adrenal medulla and the sympathetic nervous system are closely interrelated, specifically because the cells of the adrenal medulla and the postganglionic axons of the sympathetic nervous system both release catecholamines. This experiment demonstrates the effects of epinephrine on the frog heart.

⚠ 1. Obtain a frog, dissecting instruments and tray, disposable gloves, frog Ringer's solution, and dropper bottle of 1:1000 epinephrine solution. Bring them to your laboratory bench and don the gloves before beginning step 2.

2. Destroy the nervous system of the frog. (A frog used in the experiment on pituitary hormone effects may be used if your test results have already been obtained and are positive. Otherwise, obtain another frog.) Insert one blade of a scissors into its mouth as far as possible and quickly cut off the top of its head, posterior to the eyes. Then identify the spinal cavity and insert a dissecting needle into it to destroy the spinal cord.

3. Place the frog dorsal side down on a dissecting tray, and carefully open its ventral body cavity by making a vertical incision with the scissors.

4. Identify the beating heart, and carefully cut through the saclike pericardium to expose the heart tissue.

5. Visually count the heart rate for 1 minute, and record below. Keep the heart moistened with frog Ringer's solution during this interval.

Beats per minute: _____

6. Flush the heart with epinephrine solution. Record the heartbeat rate per minute for 5 consecutive minutes.

minute 1 _____   minute 4 _____

minute 2 _____   minute 5 _____

minute 3 _____

What was the effect of epinephrine on the heart rate?

_____

Was the effect long-lived? _____

7. Dispose of the frog in an appropriate container, and clean the dissecting tray and instruments before returning them to the supply area. ▪▪

Role of Thyroid Hormone, Pituitary Hormone, Insulin, and Epinephrine: Wet Lab

Determining the Effect of Thyroid Hormone on Metabolic Rate

1. In the measurement of oxygen consumption in rats, which group had the highest metabolic rate?

_____ Which group had the lowest metabolic rate? _____

Correlate these observations with the pretreatment these animals received. _____

_____

_____

Which group of rats was hyperthyroid? _____

Which euthyroid? _____ Which hypothyroid? _____

2. Since oxygen used = carbon dioxide generated, how do you know that what you measured was oxygen consumption?

_____

_____

3. What did changes in the fluid levels in the manometer arms indicate? _____

_____

4. The techniques used in this set of laboratory experiments probably permitted several inaccuracies. One was the inability to control the activity of the rats. How would changes in their activity levels affect the results observed?

_____

_____

Another possible source of error was the lack of control over the amount of food consumed by the rats in the 14-day period preceding the laboratory session. If each of the rats had been force-fed equivalent amounts of food in that 14-day period, which group (do you think) would have gained the most weight?

_____ Which the least? _____

Explain your answers. _____

_____

_____

5. TSH, produced by the anterior pituitary, causes the thyroid gland to release thyroid hormone to the blood. Which group of

rats can be assumed to have the *highest* blood levels of TSH? _____ Which the lowest? _____

Explain your reasoning. _____

_____

6. Use an appropriate reference to determine how each of the following factors modifies metabolic rate. Indicate increase by
↑ and decrease by ↓.

increased exercise _____   aging _____   infection/fever _____

small/slight stature _____   obesity _____   sex ($\male$ or $\female$) _____

Determining the Effect of Pituitary Hormones on the Ovary

7. In the experiment on the effects of pituitary hormones, two anterior pituitary hormones caused ovulation to occur in the experimental animal. Which of these actually triggered ovulation or egg expulsion?

_____ The normal function of the second hormone involved, _____,

is to _____.

8. Why was a second frog injected with saline? _____

Observing the Effects of Hyperinsulinism

9. Briefly explain what was happening within the fish's system when the fish was immersed in the insulin solution.

_____

_____

10. What is the mechanism of the recovery process observed? _____

_____

11. What would you do to help a friend who had inadvertently taken an overdose of insulin? _____

_____ Why? _____

_____

Testing the Effect of Epinephrine on the Heart

12. Based on your observations, what is the effect of epinephrine on the heart rate?

_____

13. What is the role of this effect in the "fight-or-flight" response?

_____

Blood

MATERIALS

General supply area:*

☐ Disposable gloves

☐ Safety glasses (student-provided)

☐ Bucket or large beaker containing 10% household bleach solution for slide and glassware disposal

☐ Spray bottles containing 10% bleach solution

☐ Autoclave bag

☐ Designated lancet (sharps) disposal container

☐ Plasma (obtained from an animal hospital or prepared by centrifuging animal [for example, cattle or sheep] blood obtained from a biological supply house)

☐ Test tubes and test tube racks

☐ Wide-range pH paper

☐ Stained smears of human blood from a biological supply house or, if desired by the instructor, heparinized animal blood obtained from a biological supply house or an animal hospital (for example, dog blood), or EDTA-treated red cells (reference cells[†]) with blood type labels obscured (available from Immucor, Inc.)

☐ Clean microscope slides

☐ Glass stirring rods

*Note to the Instructor: See directions for handling of soiled glassware and disposable items on page 424.

[†]The blood in these kits (each containing four blood cell types—A1, A2, B, and O—individually supplied in 10-ml vials) is used to calibrate cell counters and other automated clinical laboratory equipment. This blood has been carefully screened and can be safely used by students for blood typing and determining hematocrits. It is not usable for hemoglobin determinations or coagulation studies.

Text continues on next page.

myA&P *For practice quizzes on this lab, go to www.myaandp.com.*

PAL *For access to anatomical models and more, check out Practice Anatomy Lab.*

OBJECTIVES

1. To name the two major components of blood, and to state their average percentages in whole blood.

2. To describe the composition and functional importance of plasma.

3. To define *formed elements* and list the cell types composing them, cite their relative percentages, and describe their major functions.

4. To identify red blood cells, basophils, eosinophils, monocytes, lymphocytes, and neutrophils when provided with a microscopic preparation or appropriate diagram.

5. To provide the normal values for a total white blood cell count and a total red blood cell count, and to state the importance of these tests.

6. To conduct the following blood tests in the laboratory, and to state their norms and the importance of each.

    differential white blood cell count
    hematocrit
    hemoglobin determination
    clotting time
    ABO and Rh blood typing
    plasma cholesterol concentration

7. To discuss the reason for transfusion reactions resulting from the administration of mismatched blood.

8. To define *leukocytosis, leukopenia, leukemia, polycythemia,* and *anemia* and to cite a possible reason for each condition.

PRE-LAB QUIZ

1. Circle True or False. There are no special precautions that I need to observe when performing today's lab.

2. Three types of formed elements found in blood include erythrocytes, leucocytes, and _____.
    a. electrolytes   c. platelets
    b. fibers   d. sodium salts

3. Circle the correct term. Mature <u>erythrocytes / leucocytes</u> are the most numerous blood cells and do not have a nucleus.

4. The least numerous but largest of all agranulocytes is the
    a. basophil   c. monocyte
    b. lymphocyte   d. neutrophil

5. _____ are the leukocytes responsible for releasing histamine and other mediators of inflammation.
    a. Basophils   c. Monocytes
    b. Eosinophils   d. Neutrophils

6. Circle the correct term. When determining the <u>hematocrit / hemoglobin</u>, you will centrifuge whole blood in order to allow the formed elements to sink to the bottom of the sample.

7. Circle the correct term. Blood typing is based on the presence of proteins known as <u>antigens / antibodies</u> on the outer surface of the red blood cell plasma membrane.

8. Circle True or False. If an individual is transfused with the wrong type blood, the recipient's antibodies react with the donor's antigens, eventually clumping and hemolyzing the donated RBCs.

☐ Wright's stain in a dropper bottle
☐ Distilled water in a dropper bottle
☐ Sterile lancets
☐ Absorbent cotton balls
☐ Alcohol swabs (wipes)
☐ Paper towels
☐ Compound microscope
☐ Immersion oil
☐ Three-dimensional models (if available) and charts of blood cells
☐ Assorted slides of white blood count pathologies labeled "Unknown Sample _____"
☐ Timer

Because many blood tests are to be conducted in this exercise, it is advisable to set up a number of appropriately labeled supply areas for the various tests, as designated below. Some needed supplies are located in the general supply area.

Note: Artificial blood prepared by Ward's Natural Science can be used for differential counts, hematocrit, and blood typing.

Activity 4: Hematocrit
☐ Heparinized capillary tubes
☐ Microhematocrit centrifuge and reading gauge (if the reading gauge is not available, a millimeter ruler may be used)
☐ Capillary tube sealer or modeling clay

Activity 5: Hemoglobin determination
☐ Hemoglobinometer, hemolysis applicator, and lens paper; or Tallquist hemoglobin scale and test paper

Activity 6: Coagulation time
☐ Capillary tubes (nonheparinized)
☐ Fine triangular file

Activity 7: Blood typing
☐ Blood typing sera (anti-A, anti-B, and anti-Rh [anti-D])

☐ Rh typing box
☐ Wax marking pencil
☐ Toothpicks
☐ Medicine dropper
☐ Blood test cards or microscope slides

Activity 8: Demonstration
☐ Microscopes set up with prepared slides demonstrating the following bone (or bone marrow) conditions: macrocytic hypochromic anemia, microcytic hypochromic anemia, sickle cell anemia, lymphocytic leukemia (chronic), and eosinophilia

Activity 9: Cholesterol measurement
☐ Cholesterol test cards and color scale
PEx PhysioEx™ 8.0 Computer Simulation on page PEx-69

In this exercise you will study plasma and formed elements of blood and conduct various hematologic tests. These tests are useful diagnostic tools for the physician because blood composition (number and types of blood cells, and chemical composition) reflects the status of many body functions and malfunctions.

⚠ **ALERT: Special precautions when handling blood.** This exercise provides information on blood from several sources: human, animal, human treated, and artificial blood. The decision to use animal blood for testing or to have students test their own blood will be made by the instructor in accordance with the educational goals of the student group. For example, for students in the nursing or laboratory technician curricula, learning how to safely handle human blood or other human wastes is essential. Whenever blood is being handled, special attention must be paid to safety precautions. Instructors who opt to use human blood are responsible for its safe handling. Precautions should be used regardless of the source of the blood. This will both teach good technique and ensure the safety of the students.

Follow exactly the safety precautions listed below.

1. Wear safety gloves at all times. Discard appropriately.

2. Wear safety glasses throughout the exercise.

3. Handle only your own, freshly let (human) blood.

4. Be sure you understand the instructions and have all supplies on hand before you begin any part of the exercise.

5. Do not reuse supplies and equipment once they have been exposed to blood.

6. Keep the lab area clean. Do not let anything that has come in contact with blood touch surfaces or other individuals in the lab. Pay attention to the location of any supplies and equipment that come into contact with blood.

7. Dispose of lancets immediately after use in a designated disposal container. Do not put them down on the lab bench, even temporarily.

8. Dispose of all used cotton balls, alcohol swabs, blotting paper, and so forth in autoclave bags and place all soiled glassware in containers of 10% bleach solution.

9. Wipe down the lab bench with 10% bleach solution when you finish.

Composition of Blood

Circulating blood is a rather viscous substance that varies from bright scarlet to a dull brick red, depending on the amount of oxygen it is carrying. The average volume of blood in the body is about 5–6 L in adult males and 4–5 L in adult females.

Blood is classified as a type of connective tissue because it consists of a nonliving fluid matrix (the **plasma**) in which living cells (**formed elements**) are suspended. The fibers typical of a connective tissue matrix become visible in blood only when clotting occurs. They then appear as fibrin threads, which form the structural basis for clot formation.

More than 100 different substances are dissolved or suspended in plasma (Figure 29A.1), which is over 90% water. These include nutrients, gases, hormones, various wastes and metabolites, many types of proteins, and electrolytes. The composition of plasma varies continuously as cells remove or add substances to the blood.

Three types of formed elements are present in blood (Table 29A.1). Most numerous are **erythrocytes,** or **red blood cells (RBCs),** which are literally sacs of hemoglobin

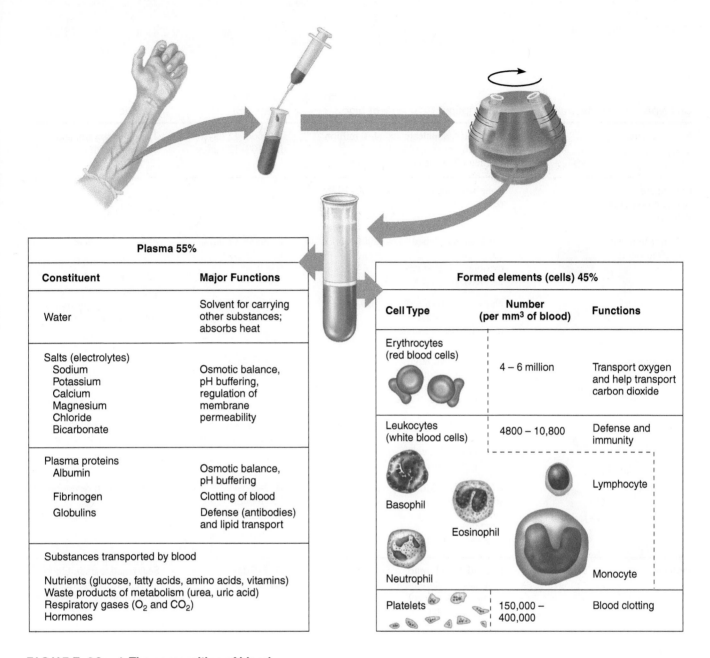

FIGURE 29A.1 **The composition of blood.**

molecules that transport the bulk of the oxygen carried in the blood (and a small percentage of the carbon dioxide). **Leukocytes,** or **white blood cells (WBCs),** are part of the body's nonspecific defenses and the immune system, and **platelets** function in hemostasis (blood clot formation). Formed elements normally constitute 45% of whole blood; plasma accounts for the remaining 55%.

A C T I V I T Y   1

Determining the Physical Characteristics of Plasma

Go to the general supply area and carefully pour a few milliliters of plasma into a test tube. Also obtain some wide-range pH paper, and then return to your laboratory bench to make the following simple observations.

pH of Plasma

Test the pH of the plasma with wide-range pH paper. Record

the pH observed. _____

Color and Clarity of Plasma

Hold the test tube up to a source of natural light. Note and record its color and degree of transparency. Is it clear, translucent, or opaque?

Color _____

Degree of transparency _____

TABLE 29A.1	Summary of Formed Elements of the Blood

Cell type	Illustration	Description*	Cells/mm³ (µl) of blood	Duration of development (D) and life span (LS)	Function
Erythrocytes (red blood cells, RBCs)		Biconcave, anucleate disc; salmon-colored; diameter 7–8 µm	4–6 million	D: about 15 days LS: 100–120 days	Transport oxygen and carbon dioxide
Leukocytes (white blood cells, WBCs)		Spherical, nucleated cells	4800–10,800		
Granulocytes Neutrophil		Nucleus multilobed; inconspicuous cytoplasmic granules; diameter 10–12 µm	3000–7000	D: about 14 days LS: 6 hours to a few days	Phagocytize bacteria
Eosinophil		Nucleus bilobed; red cytoplasmic granules; diameter 10–14 µm	100–400	D: about 14 days LS: 8–12 days	Kill parasitic worms; complex role in allergy and asthma
Basophil		Nucleus lobed; large blue-purple cytoplasmic granules; diameter 10–14 µm	20–50	D: 1–7 days LS: ? (a few hours to a few days)	Release histamine and other mediators of in-flammation; contain heparin, an anticoagulant
Agranulocytes Lymphocyte		Nucleus spherical or indented; pale blue cytoplasm; diameter 5–17 µm	1500–3000	D: days to weeks LS: hours to years	Mount immune response by direct cell attack or via antibodies
Monocyte		Nucleus U- or kidney-shaped; gray-blue cytoplasm; diameter 14–24 µm	100–700	D: 2–3 days LS: months	Phagocytosis; develop into macrophages in tissues
Platelets		Discoid cytoplasmic fragments containing granules; stain deep purple; diameter 2–4 µm	150,000–400,000	D: 4–5 days LS: 5–10 days	Seal small tears in blood vessels; instrumental in blood clotting

*Appearance when stained with Wright's stain.

Consistency

While wearing gloves, dip your finger and thumb into plasma and then press them firmly together for a few seconds. Gently pull them apart. How would you describe the consistency of plasma (slippery, watery, sticky, granular)? Record your observations.

_____

Examining the Formed Elements of Blood Microscopically

In this section, you will observe blood cells on an already prepared (purchased) blood slide or on a slide prepared from your own blood or blood provided by your instructor.

• Those using the purchased blood slide are to obtain a slide and begin their observations at step 6.

• Those testing blood provided by a biological supply source or an animal hospital are to obtain a tube of the supplied blood, disposable gloves, and the supplies listed in

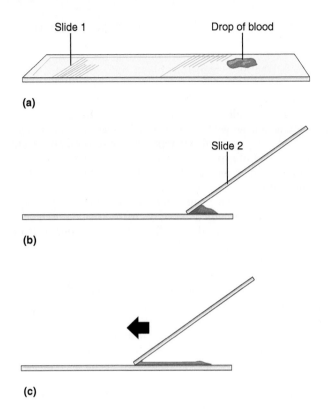

(a)

Slide 1   Drop of blood

(b)

Slide 2

(c)

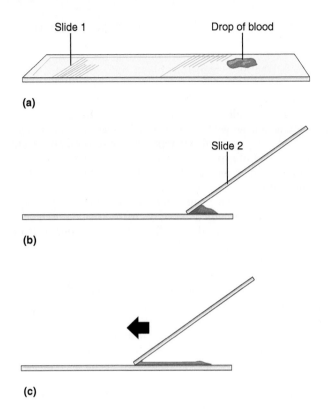

FIGURE 29A.2 Procedure for making a blood smear. (a) Place a drop of blood on slide 1 approximately ½ inch from one end. **(b)** Hold slide 2 at a 30° to 40° angle to slide 1 (it should touch the drop of blood) and allow blood to spread along entire bottom edge of angled slide. **(c)** Smoothly advance slide 2 to end of slide 1 (blood should run out before reaching the end of slide 1). Then lift slide 2 away from slide 1 and place it on a paper towel.

step 1, except for the lancets and alcohol swabs. After donning gloves, those students will go to step 3b to begin their observations.

• If you are examining your own blood, you will perform all the steps described below *except* step 3b.

1. Obtain two glass slides, a glass stirring rod, dropper bottles of Wright's stain and distilled water, two or three lancets, cotton balls, and alcohol swabs. Bring this equipment to the laboratory bench. Clean the slides thoroughly and dry them.

2. Open the alcohol swab packet and scrub your third or fourth finger with the swab. (Because the pricked finger may be a little sore later, it is better to prepare a finger on the nondominant hand.) Circumduct your hand (swing it in a cone-shaped path) for 10 to 15 seconds. This will dry the alcohol and cause your fingers to become engorged with blood. Then, open the lancet packet and grasp the lancet by its blunt end. Quickly jab the pointed end into the prepared finger to produce a free flow of blood. It is *not* a good idea to squeeze or "milk" the finger, as this forces out tissue fluid as well as blood. If the blood is not flowing freely, another puncture should be made.

! *Under no circumstances is a lancet to be used for more than one puncture.* Dispose of the lancets in the designated disposal container immediately after use.

3a. With a cotton ball, wipe away the first drop of blood; then allow another large drop of blood to form. Touch the blood to one of the cleaned slides approximately 1.3 cm, or ½ inch, from the end. Then quickly (to prevent clotting) use the second slide to form a blood smear as shown in Figure 29A.2. When properly prepared, the blood smear is uniformly thin. If the blood smear appears streaked, the blood probably began to clot or coagulate before the smear was made, and another slide should be prepared. Continue at step 4.

3b. Dip a glass rod in the blood provided, and transfer a generous drop of blood to the end of a cleaned microscope slide. For the time being, lay the glass rod on a paper towel on the bench. Then, as described in step 3a and Figure 29A.2, use the second slide to make your blood smear.

4. Dry the slide by waving it in the air. When it is completely dry, it will look dull. Place it on a paper towel, and flood it with Wright's stain. Count the number of drops of stain used. Allow the stain to remain on the slide for 3 to 4 minutes, and then flood the slide with an equal number of drops of distilled water. Allow the water and Wright's stain mixture to remain on the slide for 4 or 5 minutes or until a metallic green film or scum is apparent on the fluid surface. Blow on the slide gently every minute or so to keep the water and stain mixed during this interval.

5. Rinse the slide with a stream of distilled water. Then flood it with distilled water, and allow it to lie flat until the slide becomes translucent and takes on a pink cast. Then stand the slide on its long edge on the paper towel, and allow it to dry completely. Once the slide is dry, you can begin your observations.

6. Obtain a microscope and scan the slide under low power to find the area where the blood smear is the thinnest. After scanning the slide in low power to find the areas with the largest numbers of nucleated WBCs, read the following descriptions of cell types, and find each one on Figure 29A.1 and Table 29A.1. (The formed elements are also shown in Figure 29A.3 and Figure 29A.4.) Then, switch to

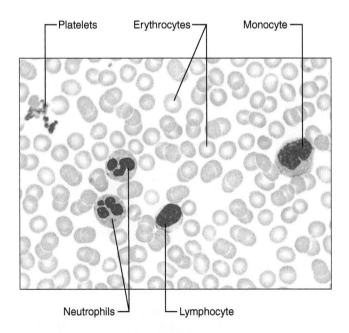

Platelets   Erythrocytes   Monocyte

Neutrophils   Lymphocyte

FIGURE 29A.3 Photomicrograph of a human blood smear stained with Wright's stain (610×).

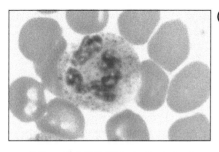

(a) Neutrophil;
multilobed nucleus

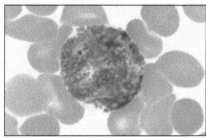

(b) Eosinophil;
bilobed nucleus,
red cytoplasmic
granules

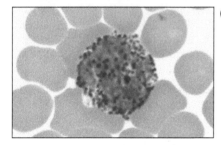

(c) Basophil;
bilobed nucleus,
purplish-black
cytoplasmic
granules

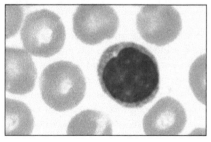

(d) Small lymphocyte;
large spherical
nucleus

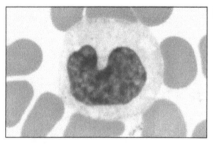

(e) Monocyte;
kidney-shaped
nucleus

FIGURE 29A.4 Leukocytes. In each case the leukocytes are surrounded by erythrocytes (1850×, Wright's stain).

the oil immersion lens, and observe the slide carefully to identify each cell type.

7.   Set your prepared slide aside for use in Activity 3.

Erythrocytes

Erythrocytes, or red blood cells, which average 7.5 μm in diameter, vary in color from a salmon red color to pale pink, depending on the effectiveness of the stain. They have a dis-

tinctive biconcave disc shape and appear paler in the center than at the edge (see Figure 29A.3).

As you observe the slide, notice that the red blood cells are by far the most numerous blood cells seen in the field. Their number averages 4.5 million to 5.5 million cells per cubic millimeter of blood (for women and men, respectively).

Red blood cells differ from the other blood cells because they are anucleate when mature and circulating in the blood. As a result, they are unable to reproduce or repair damage and have a limited life span of 100 to 120 days, after which they begin to fragment and are destroyed in the spleen and other reticuloendothelial tissues of the body.

In various anemias, the red blood cells may appear pale (an indication of decreased hemoglobin content) or may be nucleated (an indication that the bone marrow is turning out cells prematurely). ■

Leukocytes

Leukocytes, or white blood cells, are nucleated cells that are formed in the bone marrow from the same stem cells (*hemocytoblast*) as red blood cells. They are much less numerous than the red blood cells, averaging from 4800 to 10,800 cells per cubic millimeter. Basically, white blood cells are protective, pathogen-destroying cells that are transported to all parts of the body in the blood or lymph. Important to their protective function is their ability to move in and out of blood vessels, a process called **diapedesis,** and to wander through body tissues by **amoeboid motion** to reach sites of inflammation or tissue destruction. They are classified into two major groups, depending on whether or not they contain conspicuous granules in their cytoplasm.

Granulocytes make up the first group. The granules in their cytoplasm stain differentially with Wright's stain, and they have peculiarly lobed nuclei, which often consist of expanded nuclear regions connected by thin strands of nucleoplasm. There are three types of granulocytes:

Neutrophil: The most abundant of the white blood cells (50% to 70% of the leukocyte population); nucleus consists of 3 to 6 lobes and the pale lilac cytoplasm contains fine cytoplasmic granules, which are generally indistinguishable and take up both the acidic (red) and basic (blue) dyes (*neutrophil* = neutral loving); functions as an active phagocyte. The number of neutrophils increases exponentially during acute infections. (See Figure 29A.4a.)

Eosinophil: Represents 2% to 4% of the leukocyte population; nucleus is generally figure-8 or bilobed in shape; contains large cytoplasmic granules (elaborate lysosomes) that stain redorange with the acid dyes in Wright's stain (see Figure 29A.4b). Eosinophils are about the size of neutrophils and play a role in counterattacking parasitic worms. Eosinophils have complex roles in many other diseases, especially in allergy and asthma.

Basophil: Least abundant leukocyte type representing less than 1% of the population; large U- or S-shaped nucleus with two or more indentations. Cytoplasm contains coarse, sparse granules that are stained deep purple by the basic dyes in Wright's stain (see Figure 29A.4c). The granules contain several chemicals, including histamine, a vasodilator that is discharged on exposure to antigens and helps mediate the inflammatory response. Basophils are about the size of neutrophils.

The second group, **agranulocytes,** or **agranular leukocytes,** contains no *visible* cytoplasmic granules. Although found in the bloodstream, they are much more abundant in lymphoid tissues. Their nuclei tend to be closer to the norm, that is, spherical, oval, or kidney-shaped. Specific characteristics of the two types of agranulocytes are listed below.

Lymphocyte: The smallest of the leukocytes, approximately the size of a red blood cell (see Figure 29A.4d). The nucleus stains dark blue to purple, is generally spherical or slightly indented, and accounts for most of the cell mass. Sparse cytoplasm appears as a thin blue rim around the nucleus. Concerned with immunologic responses in the body; one population, the *B lymphocytes,* gives rise to *plasma cells* that produce antibodies released to blood. The second population, *T lymphocytes,* plays a regulatory role and destroys grafts, tumors, and virus-infected cells. Represents 25% or more of the WBC population.

Monocyte: The largest of the leukocytes; approximately twice the size of red blood cells (see Figure 29A.4e). Represents 3% to 8% of the leukocyte population. Dark blue nucleus is generally kidney-shaped; abundant cytoplasm stains gray-blue. Once in the tissues, monocytes convert to macrophages, active phagocytes (the "long-term cleanup team"), increasing dramatically in number during chronic infections such as tuberculosis.

Students are often asked to list the leukocytes in order from the most abundant to the least abundant. The following silly phrase may help you with this task: *Never let monkeys eat bananas* (neutrophils, lymphocytes, monocytes, eosinophils, basophils).

Platelets

Platelets are cell fragments of large multinucleate cells (**megakaryocytes**) formed in the bone marrow. They appear as darkly staining, irregularly shaped bodies interspersed among the blood cells (see Figure 29A.3). The normal platelet count in blood ranges from 150,000 to 400,000 per cubic millimeter. Platelets are instrumental in the clotting process that occurs in plasma when blood vessels are ruptured.

After you have identified these cell types on your slide, observe charts and three-dimensional models of blood cells if these are available. Do not dispose of your slide, as you will use it later for the differential white blood cell count. ▬

Hematologic Tests

When someone enters a hospital as a patient, several hematologic tests are routinely done to determine general level of health as well as the presence of pathologic conditions. You will be conducting the most common of these tests in this exercise.

⚠ Materials such as cotton balls, lancets, and alcohol swabs are used in nearly all of the following diagnostic tests. These supplies are at the general supply area and should be properly disposed of (glassware to the bleach bucket, lancets in a designated disposal container, and disposable items to the autoclave bag) immediately after use.

Other necessary supplies and equipment are at specific supply areas marked according to the test with which they are used. Since nearly all of the tests require a finger stab, if you will be using your own blood it might be wise to quickly read through the tests to determine in which instances more than one preparation can be done from the same finger stab. A little planning will save you the discomfort of a multiple-punctured finger.

An alternative to using blood obtained from the finger stab technique is using heparinized blood samples supplied by your instructor. The purpose of using heparinized tubes is to prevent the blood from clotting. Thus blood collected and stored in such tubes will be suitable for all tests except coagulation time testing.

Total White and Red Blood Cell Counts

A **total WBC count** or **total RBC count** determines the total number of that cell type per unit volume of blood. Total WBC and RBC counts are a routine part of any physical exam. Most clinical agencies use computers to conduct these counts. Since the hand counting technique typically done in college labs is rather outdated, total RBC and WBC counts will not be done here, but the importance of such counts (both normal and abnormal values) is briefly described below.

Total White Blood Cell Count

Since white blood cells are an important part of the body's defense system, it is essential to note any abnormalities in them. **Leukocytosis,** an abnormally high WBC count, may indicate bacterial or viral infection, metabolic disease, hemorrhage, or poisoning by drugs or chemicals. A decrease in the white cell number below 4000/mm³ (**leukopenia**) may indicate typhoid fever, measles, infectious hepatitis or cirrhosis, tuberculosis, or excessive antibiotic or X-ray therapy. A person with leukopenia lacks the usual protective mechanisms. **Leukemia,** a malignant disorder of the lymphoid tissues characterized by uncontrolled proliferation of abnormal WBCs accompanied by a reduction in the number of RBCs and platelets, is detectable not only by a total WBC count but also by a differential WBC count. ▪

Total Red Blood Cell Count

Since RBCs are absolutely necessary for oxygen transport, a doctor typically investigates any excessive change in their number immediately. An increase in the number of RBCs (**polycythemia**) may result from bone marrow cancer or from living at high altitudes where less oxygen is available. A decrease in the number of RBCs results in anemia. (The term **anemia** simply indicates a decreased oxygen-carrying capacity of blood that may result from a decrease in RBC number or size or a decreased hemoglobin content of the RBCs.) A decrease in RBCs may result suddenly from hemorrhage or more gradually from conditions that destroy RBCs or hinder RBC production. ▪

Differential White Blood Cell Count

To make a **differential white blood cell count,** 100 WBCs are counted and classified according to type. Such a count is routine in a physical examination and in diagnosing illness, since any abnormality or significant elevation in percentages of WBC types may indicate a problem or the source of pathology.

ACTIVITY 3

Conducting a Differential WBC Count

1.   Use the slide prepared for the identification of the blood cells in Activity 2. Begin at the edge of the smear and move the slide in a systematic manner on the microscope stage—either up and down or from side to side as indicated in Figure 29A.5.

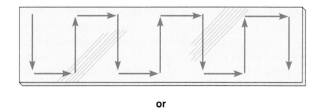

or

FIGURE 29A.5 Alternative methods of moving the slide for a differential WBC count.

2. Record each type of white blood cell you observe by making a count in the first blank column of the chart below (for example, ℍℍ ‖ = 7 cells) until you have observed and recorded a total of 100 WBCs. Using the following equation, compute the percentage of each WBC type counted, and record the percentages on the Hematologic Test Data Sheet on page 436.

$$\text{Percent (\%)} = \frac{\text{\# observed}}{\text{Total \# counted (100)}} \times 100$$

3. Select a slide marked "Unknown sample," record the slide number, and use the count chart below to conduct a differential count. Record the percentages on the data sheet on page 436.

How does the differential count from the unknown sample slide compare to a normal count?

_____

_____

Count of 100 WBCs		
	Number observed	
Cell type	Student blood smear	Unknown sample # ___
Neutrophils		
Eosinophils		
Basophils		
Lymphocytes		
Monocytes		

Using the text and other references, try to determine the blood pathology on the unknown slide. Defend your answer.

_____

_____

4. How does your differential white blood cell count correlate with the percentages given for each type on pages 428–429?

_____ ▬

Hematocrit

The **hematocrit,** or **packed cell volume (PCV),** is routinely determined when anemia is suspected. Centrifuging whole blood spins the formed elements to the bottom of the tube, with plasma forming the top layer (see Figure 29A.1). Since the blood cell population is primarily RBCs, the PCV is generally considered equivalent to the RBC volume, and this is the only value reported. However, the relative percentage of WBCs can be differentiated, and both WBC and plasma volume will be reported here. Normal hematocrit values for the male and female, respectively, are 47.0 ± 7 and 42.0 ± 5.

ACTIVITY 4

Determining the Hematocrit

The hematocrit is determined by the micromethod, so only a drop of blood is needed. If possible (and the centrifuge allows), all members of the class should prepare their capillary tubes at the same time so the centrifuge can be run only once.

1. Obtain two heparinized capillary tubes, capillary tube sealer or modeling clay, a lancet, alcohol swabs, and some cotton balls.

2. If you are using your own blood, cleanse a finger, and allow the blood to flow freely. Wipe away the first few drops and, holding the red-line-marked end of the capillary tube to the blood drop, allow the tube to fill at least three-fourths full by capillary action (Figure 29A.6a). If the blood is not flowing freely, the end of the capillary tube will not be completely submerged in the blood during filling, air will enter, and you will have to prepare another sample.

If you are using instructor-provided blood, simply immerse the red-marked end of the capillary tube in the blood sample and fill it three-quarters full as just described.

3. Plug the blood-containing end by pressing it into the capillary tube sealer or clay (Figure 29A.6b). Prepare a second tube in the same manner.

4. Place the prepared tubes opposite one another in the radial grooves of the microhematocrit centrifuge with the sealed ends abutting the rubber gasket at the centrifuge periphery (Figure 29A.6c). This loading procedure balances the centrifuge and prevents blood from spraying everywhere by centrifugal force. *Make a note of the numbers of the grooves your tubes are in.* When all the tubes have been loaded, make sure the centrifuge is properly balanced, and secure the centrifuge cover. Turn the centrifuge on, and set the timer for 4 or 5 minutes.

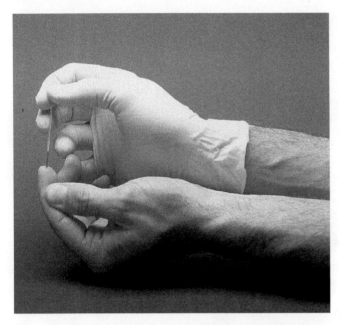

(a)

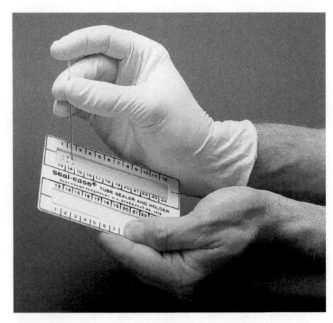

(b)

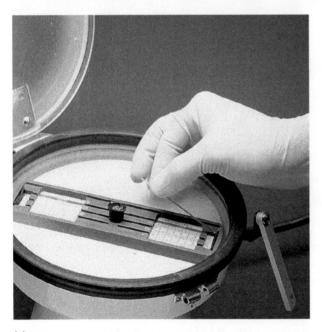

(c)

FIGURE 29A.6 Steps in a hematocrit determination.
(a) Load a heparinized capillary tube with blood. **(b)** Plug the blood-containing end of the tube with clay. **(c)** Place the tube in a microhematocrit centrifuge. (Centrifuge must be balanced.)

5. Determine the percentage of RBCs, WBCs, and plasma by using the microhematocrit reader. The RBCs are the bottom layer, the plasma is the top layer, and the WBCs are the buff-colored layer between the two. If the reader is not available, use a millimeter ruler to measure the length of the filled capillary tube occupied by each element, and compute its percentage by using the following formula:

$$\frac{\text{Height of the column composed of the element (mm)}}{\text{Height of the original column of whole blood (mm)}} \times 100$$

Record your calculations below and on the data sheet on page 436.

% RBC _____ % WBC _____ % plasma _____

Usually WBCs constitute 1% of the total blood volume. How do your blood values compare to this figure and to the normal percentages for RBCs and plasma? (See page 425.)

_____

As a rule, a hematocrit is considered a more accurate test than the total RBC count for determining the RBC composition of the blood. A hematocrit within the normal range generally indicates a normal RBC number, whereas an abnormally high or low hematocrit is cause for concern. ▪

Hemoglobin Concentration

As noted earlier, a person can be anemic even with a normal RBC count. Since hemoglobin (Hb) is the RBC protein responsible for oxygen transport, perhaps the most accurate way of measuring the oxygen-carrying capacity of the blood is to determine its hemoglobin content. Oxygen, which combines reversibly with the heme (iron-containing portion) of the hemoglobin molecule, is picked up by the blood cells in the lungs and unloaded in the tissues. Thus, the more hemoglobin molecules the RBCs contain, the more oxygen they will be able to transport. Normal blood contains 12 to 18 g of hemoglobin per 100 ml of blood. Hemoglobin content in men is slightly higher (13 to 18 g) than in women (12 to 16 g).

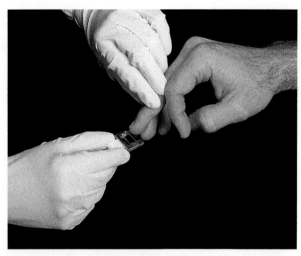

(a) A drop of blood is added to the moat plate of the blood chamber. The blood must flow freely.

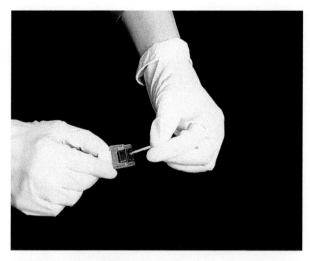

(b) The blood sample is hemolyzed with a wooden hemolysis applicator. Complete hemolysis requires 35 to 45 seconds.

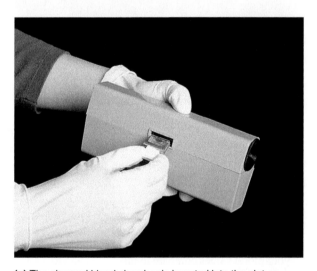

(c) The charged blood chamber is inserted into the slot on the side of the hemoglobinometer.

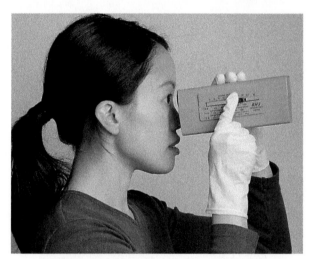

(d) The colors of the green split screen are found by moving the slide with the right index finger. When the two colors match in density, the grams/100 ml and % Hb are read on the scale.

FIGURE 29A.7 Hemoglobin determination using a hemoglobinometer.

Determining Hemoglobin Concentration

Several techniques have been developed to estimate the hemoglobin content of blood, ranging from the old, rather inaccurate Tallquist method to expensive colorimeters, which are precisely calibrated and yield highly accurate results. Directions for both the Tallquist method and a hemoglobinometer are provided here.

Tallquist Method

1. Obtain a Tallquist hemoglobin scale, test paper, lancets, alcohol swabs, and cotton balls.

2. Use instructor-provided blood or prepare the finger as previously described. (For best results, make sure the alcohol evaporates before puncturing your finger.) Place one good-sized drop of blood on the special absorbent paper provided with the color scale. The blood stain should be larger than the holes on the color scale.

3. As soon as the blood has dried and loses its glossy appearance, match its color, under natural light, with the color standards by moving the specimen under the comparison scale so that the blood stain appears at all the various apertures. (The blood should not be allowed to dry to a brown color, as this will result in an inaccurate reading.) Because the colors on the scale represent 1% variations in hemoglobin content, it may be necessary to estimate the percentage if the color of your blood sample is intermediate between two color standards.

4. On the data sheet on page 436, record your results as the percentage of hemoglobin concentration and as grams per 100 ml of blood.

Hemoglobinometer Determination

1. Obtain a hemoglobinometer, hemolysis applicator, alcohol swab, and lens paper, and bring them to your bench. Test the hemoglobinometer light source to make sure it is working; if not, request new batteries before proceeding and test it again.

2. Remove the blood chamber from the slot in the side of the hemoglobinometer and disassemble the blood chamber by separating the glass plates from the metal clip. Notice as you do this that the larger glass plate has an H-shaped depression cut into it that acts as a moat to hold the blood, whereas the smaller glass piece is flat and serves as a coverslip.

3. Clean the glass plates with an alcohol swab, and then wipe them dry with lens paper. Hold the plates by their sides to prevent smearing during the wiping process.

4. Reassemble the blood chamber (remember: larger glass piece on the bottom with the moat up), but leave the moat plate about halfway out to provide adequate exposed surface to charge it with blood.

5. Obtain a drop of blood (from the provided sample or from your fingertip as before), and place it on the depressed area of the moat plate that is closest to you (Figure 29A.7a).

6. Using the wooden hemolysis applicator, stir or agitate the blood to rupture (lyse) the RBCs (Figure 29A.7b). This usually takes 35 to 45 seconds. Hemolysis is complete when the blood appears transparent rather than cloudy.

7. Push the blood-containing glass plate all the way into the metal clip and then firmly insert the charged blood chamber back into the slot on the side of the instrument (Figure 29A.7c).

8. Hold the hemoglobinometer in your left hand with your left thumb resting on the light switch located on the underside of the instrument. Look into the eyepiece and notice that there is a green area divided into two halves (a split field).

9. With the index finger of your right hand, slowly move the slide on the right side of the hemoglobinometer back and forth until the two halves of the green field match (Figure 29A.7d).

10. Note and record on the data sheet on page 436 the grams of Hb (hemoglobin)/100 ml of blood indicated on the uppermost scale by the index mark on the slide. Also record % Hb, indicated by one of the lower scales.

11. Disassemble the blood chamber once again, and carefully place its parts (glass plates and clip) into a bleach-containing beaker.

Generally speaking, the relationship between the PCV and grams of hemoglobin per 100 ml of blood is 3:1—for example, a PCV of 36 with 12 g of Hb per 100 ml of blood is a ratio of 3:1. How do your values compare?

Record on the data sheet (page 436) the value obtained from your data. ▪

Bleeding Time

Normally a sharp prick of the finger or earlobe results in bleeding that lasts from 2 to 7 minutes (Ivy method) or 0 to 5 minutes (Duke method), although other factors such as altitude affect the time. How long the bleeding lasts is referred to as **bleeding time** and tests the ability of platelets to stop bleeding in capillaries and small vessels. Absence of some clotting factors may affect bleeding time, but prolonged bleeding time is most often associated with deficient or abnormal platelets.

Coagulation Time

Blood clotting, or **coagulation,** is a protective mechanism that minimizes blood loss when blood vessels are ruptured. This process requires the interaction of many substances normally present in the plasma (clotting factors, or procoagulants) as well as some released by platelets and injured tissues. Basically hemostasis proceeds as follows (Figure 29A.8a): The injured tissues and platelets release **tissue factor (TF)** and **PF$_3$** respectively, which trigger the clotting mechanism, or cascade. Tissue factor and PF$_3$ interact with other blood protein clotting factors and calcium ions to form **prothrombin activator,** which in turn converts **prothrombin** (present in plasma) to **thrombin.** Thrombin then acts enzymatically to polymerize the soluble **fibrinogen** proteins (present in plasma) into insoluble **fibrin,** which forms a meshwork of strands that traps the RBCs and forms the basis of the clot (Figure 29A.8b). Normally, blood removed from the body clots within 2 to 6 minutes.

ACTIVITY 6

Determining Coagulation Time

1. Obtain a *nonheparinized* capillary tube, a timer (or watch), a lancet, cotton balls, a triangular file, and alcohol swabs.

2. Clean and prick the finger to produce a free flow of blood. Discard the lancet in the disposal container.

3. Place one end of the capillary tube in the blood drop, and hold the opposite end at a lower level to collect the sample.

4. Lay the capillary tube on a paper towel.

Record the time. _____

5. At 30-second intervals, make a small nick on the tube close to one end with the triangular file, and then carefully break the tube. Slowly separate the ends to see if a gel-like thread of fibrin spans the gap. When this occurs, record below and on the data sheet on page 436 the time for coagulation to occur. Are your results within the normal time range?

---

6. Put used supplies in the autoclave bag and broken capillary tubes into the sharps container. ▪

Blood Typing

Blood typing is a system of blood classification based on the presence of specific glycoproteins on the outer surface of the RBC plasma membrane. Such proteins are called **antigens,** or **agglutinogens,** and are genetically determined. In many cases, these antigens are accompanied by plasma proteins, **antibodies** or **agglutinins,** that react with RBCs bearing different antigens, causing them to be clumped, agglutinated, and eventually hemolyzed. It is because of this phenomenon that a person's blood must be carefully typed before a whole blood or packed cell transfusion.

Injury to lining of
vessel exposes collagen
fibers; platelets adhere

Platelet
plug forms

Fibrin clot
with trapped
red blood cells

Collagen fibers

Platelets

Fibrin

Platelets release chemicals
that make nearby platelets sticky

PF₃ from
platelets and
tissue factor
from damaged
tissue cells

+

Calcium
and other
clotting
factors
in blood
plasma

Coagulation

① Formation of
prothrombin
activator

② Prothrombin → Thrombin

③ Fibrinogen
(soluble) → Fibrin
(insoluble)

(a)

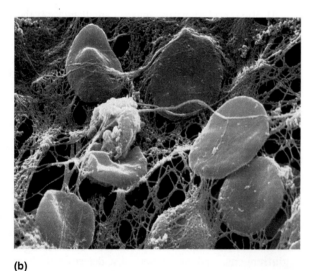

(b)

FIGURE 29A.8 Events of hemostasis and blood clotting.
(a) Simple schematic of events. Steps numbered 1–3 represent
the major events of coagulation. **(b)** Photomicrograph of RBCs
trapped in a fibrin mesh (2700×).

Several blood typing systems exist, based on the various possible antigens, but the factors routinely typed for are antigens of the ABO and Rh blood groups which are most commonly involved in transfusion reactions. Other blood factors, such as Kell, Lewis, M, and N, are not routinely typed for unless the individual will require multiple transfusions. The basis of the ABO typing is shown in Table 29A.2.

Individuals whose red blood cells carry the Rh antigen are Rh positive (approximately 85% of the U.S. population); those lacking the antigen are Rh negative. Unlike ABO blood groups, neither the blood of the Rh-positive (Rh⁺) nor Rh-negative (Rh⁻) individuals carries preformed anti-Rh antibodies. This is understandable in the case of the Rh-positive individual. However, Rh-negative persons who receive transfusions of Rh-positive blood become sensitized by the Rh antigens of the donor RBCs, and their systems begin to produce anti-Rh antibodies. On subsequent exposures to Rh-positive blood, typical transfusion reactions occur, resulting in the clumping and hemolysis of the donor blood cells.

Although the blood of dogs and other mammals does react with some of the human agglutinins (present in the antisera), the reaction is not as pronounced and varies with the animal blood used. Hence, the most accurate and predictable blood typing results are obtained with human blood. The artificial blood kit does not use any body fluids and produces results similar to but not identical to results for human blood.

ACTIVITY 7

Typing for ABO and Rh Blood Groups

Blood may be typed on glass slides or using blood test cards. Each method is described in this activity.

Typing Blood Using Glass Slides

1. Obtain two clean microscope slides, a wax marking pencil, anti-A, anti-B, and anti-Rh typing sera, toothpicks, lancets, alcohol swabs, medicine dropper, and the Rh typing box.

2. Divide slide 1 into halves with the wax marking pencil. Label the lower left-hand corner "anti-A" and the lower right-hand corner "anti-B." Mark the bottom of slide 2 "anti-Rh."

3. Place one drop of anti-A serum on the *left* side of slide 1. Place one drop of anti-B serum on the *right* side of slide 1. Place one drop of anti-Rh serum in the center of slide 2.

4. If you are using your own blood, cleanse your finger with an alcohol swab, pierce the finger with a lancet, and wipe away the first drop of blood. Obtain 3 drops of freely flowing blood, placing one drop on each side of slide 1 and a drop on slide 2. Immediately dispose of the lancet in a designated disposal container.

If using instructor-provided animal blood or EDTA-treated red cells, use a medicine dropper to place one drop of blood on each side of slide 1 and a drop of blood on slide 2.

5. Quickly mix each blood-antiserum sample with a *fresh* toothpick. Then dispose of the toothpicks and used alcohol swab in the autoclave bag.

6. Place slide 2 on the Rh typing box and rock gently back and forth. (A slightly higher temperature is required for precise Rh typing than for ABO typing.)

TABLE 29A.2	ABO Blood Typing					
				% of U.S. population		
ABO blood type	Antigens present on RBC membranes	Antibodies present in plasma		White	Black	Asian
A	A	Anti-B		40	27	28
B	B	Anti-A		11	20	27
AB	A and B	None		4	4	5
O	Neither	Anti-A and anti-B		45	49	40

7.   After 2 minutes, observe all three blood samples for evidence of clumping. The agglutination that occurs in the positive test for the Rh factor is very fine and difficult to perceive; thus if there is any question, observe the slide under the microscope. Record your observations in the Blood Typing chart.

8.   Interpret your ABO results in light of the information in Figure 29A.9. If clumping was observed on slide 2, you are Rh positive. If not, you are Rh negative.

Blood being tested   **Serum**

FIGURE 29A.9 **Blood typing of ABO blood types.** When serum containing anti-A or anti-B antibodies (agglutinins) is added to a blood sample, agglutination will occur between the antibody and the corresponding antigen (agglutinogen A or B). As illustrated, agglutination occurs with both sera in blood group AB, with anti-B serum in blood group B, with anti-A serum in blood group A, and with neither serum in blood group O.

Blood Typing		
Result	Observed (+)	Not observed (−)
Presence of clumping with anti-A		
Presence of clumping with anti-B		
Presence of clumping with anti-Rh		

9.   Record your blood type on the data sheet on page 436.

10. Put the used slides in the bleach-containing bucket at the general supply area; put disposable supplies in the autoclave bag.

Using Blood Typing Cards

1.   Obtain a blood typing card marked A, B, and Rh, dropper bottles of anti-A serum, anti-B serum, and anti-Rh serum, toothpicks, lancets, and alcohol swabs.

2.   Place a drop of anti-A serum in the spot marked anti-A, place a drop of anti-B serum on the spot marked anti-B, and place a drop of anti-Rh serum on the spot marked anti-Rh (or anti-D).

3.   Carefully add a drop of blood to each of the spots marked "Blood" on the card. If you are using your own blood, refer to step 4 in the Activity 7 section Typing Blood Using Glass Slides. Immediately discard the lancet in the designated disposal container.

4.   Using a new toothpick for each test, mix the blood sample with the antibody. Dispose of the toothpicks appropriately.

5.   Gently rock the card to allow the blood and antibodies to mix.

6.   After 2 minutes, observe the card for evidence of clumping. The Rh clumping is very fine and may be difficult to observe. Record your observations in the Blood Typing chart. Use Figure 29A.9 to interpret your results.

7.   Record your blood type on the chart on page 436, and discard the card in an autoclave bag. ■

Hematologic Test Data Sheet

Differential WBC count:

WBC	Student blood smear	Unknown sample # ___
% neutrophils	_____	_____
% eosinophils	_____	_____
% basophils	_____	_____
% monocytes	_____	_____
% lymphocytes	_____	_____

Hematocrit (PCV):

RBC _____ % of blood volume

WBC _____ % of blood volume   not generally reported

Plasma _____ % of blood

Hemoglobin (Hb) content:

Tallquist method: _____ g/100 ml of blood; _____ % Hb

Hemoglobinometer (type: _____)

_____ g/100 ml of blood; _____ %Hb

Ratio (PCV to grams of Hb per 100 ml of blood): _____

Coagulation time _____

Blood typing:

ABO group _____ Rh factor _____

Cholesterol concentration _____ mg/dl of blood

ACTIVITY 8

Observing Demonstration Slides

Before continuing on to the cholesterol determination, take the time to look at the slides of *macrocytic hypochromic anemia, microcytic hypochromic anemia, sickle cell anemia, lymphocytic leukemia* (chronic), and *eosinophilia* that have been put on demonstration by your instructor. Record your observations in the appropriate section of the Exercise 29A Review Sheet. You can refer to your notes, the text, and other references later to respond to questions about the blood pathologies represented on the slides. ▇

Cholesterol Concentration in Plasma

Atherosclerosis is the disease process in which the body's blood vessels become increasingly occluded by plaques. Because the plaques narrow the arteries, they can contribute to hypertensive heart disease. They also serve as focal points for the formation of blood clots (thrombi), which may break away and block smaller vessels farther downstream in the circulatory pathway and cause heart attacks or strokes.

Ever since medical clinicians discovered that cholesterol is a major component of the smooth muscle plaques formed during atherosclerosis, it has had a bad press. Today, virtually no physical examination of an adult is considered complete until cholesterol levels are assessed along with other lifestyle risk factors. A normal value for plasma cholesterol in adults ranges from 130 to 200 mg per 100 ml of plasma; you will use blood to make such a determination.

Although the total plasma cholesterol concentration is valuable information, it may be misleading, particularly if a person's high-density lipoprotein (HDL) level is high and

low-density lipoprotein (LDL) level is relatively low. Cholesterol, being water insoluble, is transported in the blood complexed to lipoproteins. In general, cholesterol bound into HDLs is destined to be degraded by the liver and then eliminated from the body, whereas that forming part of the LDLs is "traveling" to the body's tissue cells. When LDL levels are excessive, cholesterol is deposited in the blood vessel walls; hence, LDLs are considered to carry the "bad" cholesterol.

ACTIVITY 9

Measuring Plasma Cholesterol Concentration

1. Go to the appropriate supply area, and obtain a cholesterol test card and color scale, lancet, and alcohol swab.

2. Clean your fingertip with the alcohol swab, allow it to dry, then prick it with a lancet. Place a drop of blood on the test area of the card. Put the lancet in the designated disposal container.

3. After 3 minutes, remove the blood sample strip from the card and discard in the autoclave bag.

4. Analyze the underlying test spot, using the included color scale. Record the cholesterol level below and on the data sheet above.

Cholesterol level _____ mg/dl

⚠ 5. Before leaving the laboratory, use the spray bottle of bleach solution and saturate a paper towel to thoroughly wash down your laboratory bench. ▇

Blood

Composition of Blood

1. What is the blood volume of an average-size adult male? _____ liters An average adult female? _____ liters

2. What determines whether blood is bright red or a dull brick-red? _____

_____

3. Use the key to identify the cell type(s) or blood elements that fit the following descriptive statements.

Key: a. red blood cell   d. basophil   g. lymphocyte
       b. megakaryocyte   e. monocyte   h. formed elements
       c. eosinophil   f. neutrophil   i. plasma

_____ 1. most numerous leukocyte

_____, _____, and _____ 2. granulocytes (3)

_____ 3. also called an erythrocyte; anucleate formed element

_____, _____ 4. actively phagocytic leukocytes

_____, _____ 5. agranulocytes

_____ 6. ancestral cell of platelets

_____ 7. (a) through (g) are all examples of these

_____ 8. number rises during parasite infections

_____ 9. releases histamine; promotes inflammation

_____ 10. many formed in lymphoid tissue

_____ 11. transports oxygen

_____ 12. primarily water, noncellular; the fluid matrix of blood

_____ 13. increases in number during prolonged infections

_____, _____, _____,

_____, _____ 14. the five types of white blood cells

4. List four classes of nutrients normally found in plasma. _____ ,

_____ , _____ , and _____

Name two gases. _____ and _____

Name three ions. _____ , _____ , and _____

5. Describe the consistency and color of the plasma you observed in the laboratory. _____

_____

6. What is the average life span of a red blood cell? How does its anucleate condition affect this life span?

_____

_____

_____

7. From memory, describe the structural characteristics of each of the following blood cell types as accurately as possible, and note the percentage of each in the total white blood cell population.

eosinophils: _____

_____

neutrophils: _____

_____

lymphocytes: _____

_____

basophils: _____

_____

monocytes: _____

_____

8. Correctly identify the blood pathologies described in column A by matching them with selections from column B:

Column A   **Column B**

_____ 1. abnormal increase in the number of WBCs   a. anemia

_____ 2. abnormal increase in the number of RBCs   b. leukocytosis

_____ 3. condition of too few RBCs or of RBCs with   c. leukopenia
                              hemoglobin deficiencies

                                                                                                      d. polycythemia

_____ 4. abnormal decrease in the number of WBCs

Hematologic Tests

9. Broadly speaking, why are hematologic studies of blood so important in the diagnosis of disease?

_____

_____

10. In the chart below, record information from the blood tests you read about or conducted. Complete the chart by recording values for healthy male adults and indicating the significance of high or low values for each test.

Test	Student test results	Normal values (healthy male adults)	Significance	
			High values	Low values
Total WBC count	No data			
Total RBC count	No data			
Hematocrit				
Hemoglobin determination				
Bleeding time	No data			
Coagulation time				

11. Why is a differential WBC count more valuable than a total WBC count when trying to pin down the specific source of

pathology? _____

_____

_____

12. What name is given to the process of RBC production? _____

What hormone acts as a stimulus for this process? _____

Why might patients with kidney disease suffer from anemia? _____

_____

How can such patients be treated? _____

13. Discuss the effect of each of the following factors on RBC count. Consult an appropriate reference as necessary, and explain your reasoning.

long-term effect of athletic training (for example, running 4 to 5 miles per day over a period of six to nine months):

_____

_____

a permanent move from sea level to a high-altitude area: _____

_____

_____

14. Define *hematocrit.* _____

15. If you had a high hematocrit, would you expect your hemoglobin determination to be high or low? _____

    Why? _____

    _____

16. What is an anticoagulant? _____

    Name two anticoagulants used in conducting the hematologic tests. _____

    and _____

    What is the body's natural anticoagulant? _____

17. If your blood clumped with both anti-A and anti-B sera, your ABO blood type would be _____

    To what ABO blood groups could you give blood? _____

    From which ABO donor types could you receive blood? _____

    Which ABO blood type is most common? _____ Least common? _____

18. What blood type is theoretically considered the universal donor? _____ Why? _____

    _____

19. Assume the blood of two patients has been typed for ABO blood type.

    Typing results
    Mr. Adams:

    Blood drop and anti-A serum   Blood drop and anti-B serum

    Typing results
    Mr. Calhoon:

    Blood drop and anti-A serum   Blood drop and anti-B serum

    On the basis of these results, Mr. Adams has type _____ blood, and Mr. Calhoon has type _____ blood.

20. Explain why an Rh-negative person does not have a transfusion reaction on the first exposure to Rh-positive blood but *does*

have a reaction on the second exposure. _____

_____

What happens when an ABO blood type is mismatched for the first time? _____

_____

21. Record your observations of the five demonstration slides viewed.

a. Macrocytic hypochromic anemia: _____

b. Microcytic hypochromic anemia: _____

_____

c. Sickle cell anemia: _____

d. Lymphocytic leukemia (chronic): _____

_____

e. Eosinophilia: _____

Which of the slides above (a through e) corresponds with the following conditions?

_____ 1. iron-deficient diet   _____ 4. lack of vitamin B_{12}

_____ 2. a type of bone marrow cancer   _____ 5. a tapeworm infestation in the body

_____ 3. genetic defect that causes hemoglobin   _____ 6. a bleeding ulcer
              to become sharp/spiky

22. Provide the normal, or at least "desirable," range for plasma cholesterol concentration.

_____ mg/100 ml

23. Describe the relationship between high blood cholesterol levels and cardiovascular diseases such as hypertension, heart attacks, and strokes.

_____

_____

_____

_____

_____

Anatomy of the Heart

MATERIALS

- [ ] X ray of the human thorax for observation of the position of the heart in situ; X-ray viewing box
- [ ] Three-dimensional heart model and torso model or laboratory chart showing heart anatomy
- [ ] Red and blue pencils
- [ ] Highlighter
- [ ] Three-dimensional models of cardiac and skeletal muscle
- [ ] Compound microscope
- [ ] Prepared slides of cardiac muscle (l.s.)
- [ ] Preserved sheep heart, pericardial sacs intact (if possible)
- [ ] Dissecting instruments and tray
- [ ] Pointed glass rods or blunt probes
- [ ] Plastic rulers
- [ ] Disposable gloves
- [ ] Container for disposal of organic debris
- [ ] Laboratory detergent
- [ ] Spray bottle with 10% household bleach solution
- [ ] *Human Cardiovascular System: The Heart* videotape

myA&P *For practice quizzes on this lab, go to www.myaandp.com.*

PAL *For access to anatomical models and more, check out Practice Anatomy Lab.*

OBJECTIVES

1. To describe the location of the heart.
2. To name and locate the major anatomical areas and structures of the heart when provided with an appropriate model, diagram, or dissected sheep heart, and to explain the function of each.
3. To trace the pathway of blood through the heart.
4. To explain why the heart is called a double pump, and to compare the pulmonary and systemic circuits.
5. To explain the operation of the atrioventricular and semilunar valves.
6. To trace the functional blood supply of the heart and name the associated blood vessels.
7. To describe the histology of cardiac muscle, and to note the importance of its intercalated discs and the spiral arrangement of its cells.

PRE-LAB QUIZ

1. The heart is enclosed in a double-walled sac called the
   a. apex
   b. mediastinum
   c. pericardium
   d. thorax
2. The heart is divided into _____ chambers.
   a. two
   b. three
   c. four
   d. five
3. What is the name of the two receiving chambers of the heart?
   _____
4. The left ventricle discharges blood into the _____, from which all systemic arteries of the body diverge to supply the body tissues.
   a. aorta
   b. pulmonary artery
   c. pulmonary vein
   d. vena cava
5. Circle True or False. Blood flows through the heart in one direction—from the atria to the ventricles.
6. Circle the correct term. The right atrioventricular valve, or tricuspid / mitral, prevents backflow into the right atrium when the right ventricle is contracting.
7. Circle the correct term. The heart serves as a double pump. The right / left side serves as the pulmonary circulation pump, shunting carbon dioxide–rich blood to the lungs.
8. The functional blood supply of the heart itself is provided by the
   a. aorta
   b. carotid arteries
   c. coronary arteries
   d. pulmonary trunk
9. Two microscopic features of cardiac cells that help distinguish them from other types of muscle cells are branching and
   a. intercalated discs
   b. myosin fibers
   c. sarcolemma
   d. striations
10. Circle the correct term. In the heart, the left / right ventricle has thicker walls and a basically circular cavity shape.

The major function of the **cardiovascular system** is transportation. Using blood as the transport vehicle, the system carries oxygen, digested foods, cell wastes, electrolytes, and many other substances vital to the body's homeostasis to and from the body cells. The system's propulsive force is the contracting heart, which can be compared to a muscular pump equipped with one-way valves. As the heart contracts, it forces blood into a closed system of large and small plumbing tubes (blood vessels) within which the blood is confined and circulated. This exercise deals with the structure of the heart, or circulatory pump. The anatomy of the blood vessels is considered separately in Exercise 32.

Gross Anatomy of the Human Heart

The **heart,** a cone-shaped organ approximately the size of a fist, is located within the mediastinum, or medial cavity, of the thorax. It is flanked laterally by the lungs, posteriorly by the vertebral column, and anteriorly by the sternum (Figure 30.1). Its more pointed **apex** extends slightly to the left and rests on the diaphragm, approximately at the level of the fifth intercostal space. Its broader **base,** from which the great vessels emerge, lies beneath the second rib and points toward the right shoulder. In situ, the right ventricle of the heart forms most of its anterior surface.

The apical pulse may be heard in the 5th intercostal space at the point of maximal intensity (PMI).

● If an X ray of a human thorax is available, verify the relationships described above; otherwise, Figure 30.1 should suffice.

The heart is enclosed within a double-walled fibroserous sac called the pericardium. The thin **epicardium,** or **visceral pericardium,** is closely applied to the heart muscle. It reflects downward at the base of the heart to form its companion serous membrane, the outer, loosely applied **parietal pericardium,** which is attached at the heart apex to the diaphragm. Serous fluid produced by these membranes allows the heart to beat in a relatively frictionless environment. The serous parietal pericardium, in turn, lines the loosely fitting superficial **fibrous pericardium** composed of dense connective tissue.

Inflammation of the pericardium, **pericarditis,** causes painful adhesions between the serous pericardial layers. These adhesions interfere with heart movements. ■

The walls of the heart are composed primarily of cardiac muscle—the **myocardium**—which is reinforced internally by a dense fibrous connective tissue network. This network—the *fibrous skeleton of the heart*—is more elaborate and thicker in certain areas, for example, around the valves and at the base of the great vessels leaving the heart.

Figure 30.2 shows three views of the heart—external anterior and posterior views and a frontal section. As its anatomical areas are described in the text, consult the figure.

Heart Chambers

The heart is divided into four chambers: two superior **atria** (singular: *atrium*) and two inferior **ventricles,** each lined by thin serous endothelium called the **endocardium.** The septum that divides the heart longitudinally is referred to as the **interatrial** or **interventricular septum,** depending on which chambers it partitions. Functionally, the atria are receiving chambers and are relatively ineffective as pumps. Blood flows into the atria under low pressure from the veins of the body. The right atrium receives relatively oxygen-poor blood from the body via the **superior** and **inferior venae cavae** and the coronary sinus. Four **pulmonary veins** deliver oxygen-rich blood from the lungs to the left atrium.

The inferior thick-walled ventricles, which form the bulk of the heart, are the discharging chambers. They force blood out of the heart into the large arteries that emerge from its base. The right ventricle pumps blood into the **pulmonary trunk,** which routes blood to the lungs to be oxygenated. The left ventricle discharges blood into the **aorta,** from which all systemic arteries of the body diverge to supply the body tissues. Discussions of the heart's pumping action usually refer to ventricular activity.

Heart Valves

Four valves enforce a one-way blood flow through the heart chambers. The **atrioventricular (AV) valves,** located between the atrial and ventricular chambers on each side, prevent backflow into the atria when the ventricles are contracting. The left atrioventricular valve, also called the **mitral** or *bicuspid valve,* consists of two cusps, or flaps, of endocardium. The right atrioventricular valve, the **tricuspid valve,** has three cusps (Figure 30.3). Tiny white collagenic cords called the **chordae tendineae** (literally, heart strings) anchor the cusps to the ventricular walls. The chordae tendineae originate from small bundles of cardiac muscle, called **papillary muscles,** that project from the myocardial wall (see Figure 30.2b).

When blood is flowing passively into the atria and then into the ventricles during **diastole** (the period of ventricular filling), the AV valve flaps hang limply into the ventricular chambers and then are carried passively toward the atria by the accumulating blood. When the ventricles contract **(systole)** and compress the blood in their chambers, the intraventricular blood pressure rises, causing the valve flaps to be reflected superiorly, which closes the AV valves. The chordae tendineae, pulled taut by the contracting papillary muscles, anchor the flaps in a closed position that prevents backflow into the atria during ventricular contraction. If unanchored,

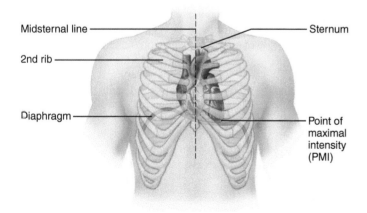

Midsternal line ——————

2nd rib ——————

Diaphragm ——————

———— Sternum

———— Point of maximal intensity (PMI)

FIGURE 30.1 Location of the heart in the thorax.

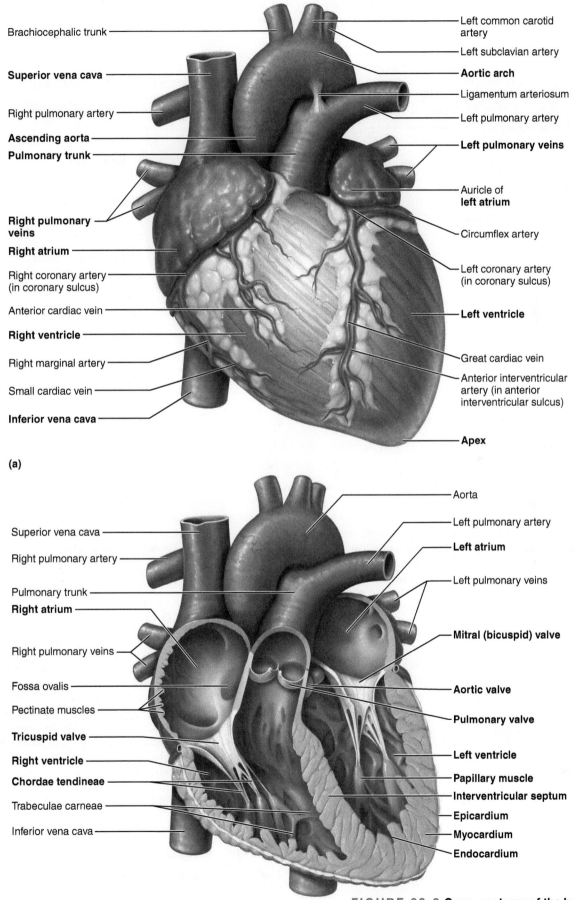

Brachiocephalic trunk

Superior vena cava

Right pulmonary artery

Ascending aorta

Pulmonary trunk

Right pulmonary veins

Right atrium

Right coronary artery (in coronary sulcus)

Anterior cardiac vein

Right ventricle

Right marginal artery

Small cardiac vein

Inferior vena cava

Left common carotid artery

Left subclavian artery

Aortic arch

Ligamentum arteriosum

Left pulmonary artery

Left pulmonary veins

Auricle of left atrium

Circumflex artery

Left coronary artery (in coronary sulcus)

Left ventricle

Great cardiac vein

Anterior interventricular artery (in anterior interventricular sulcus)

Apex

(a)

Superior vena cava

Right pulmonary artery

Pulmonary trunk

Right atrium

Right pulmonary veins

Fossa ovalis

Pectinate muscles

Tricuspid valve

Right ventricle

Chordae tendineae

Trabeculae carneae

Inferior vena cava

Aorta

Left pulmonary artery

Left atrium

Left pulmonary veins

Mitral (bicuspid) valve

Aortic valve

Pulmonary valve

Left ventricle

Papillary muscle

Interventricular septum

Epicardium

Myocardium

Endocardium

(b)

FIGURE 30.2 Gross anatomy of the human heart. (a) External anterior view. **(b)** Frontal section.

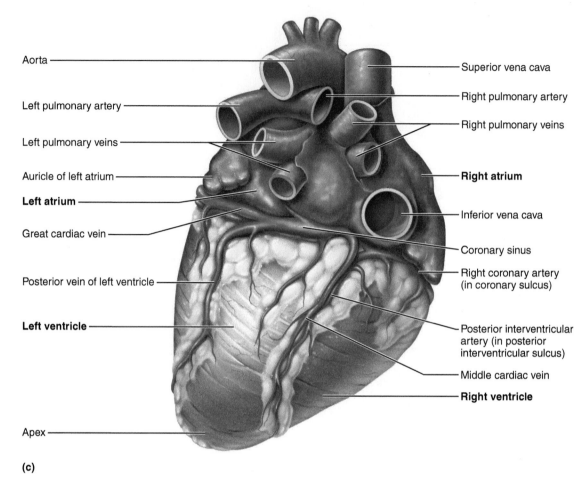

Aorta

Left pulmonary artery

Left pulmonary veins

Auricle of left atrium

Left atrium

Great cardiac vein

Posterior vein of left ventricle

Left ventricle

Apex

Superior vena cava

Right pulmonary artery

Right pulmonary veins

Right atrium

Inferior vena cava

Coronary sinus

Right coronary artery (in coronary sulcus)

Posterior interventricular artery (in posterior interventricular sulcus)

Middle cardiac vein

Right ventricle

(c)

FIGURE 30.2 (continued) Gross anatomy of the human heart. (c) Exterior posterior view.

the flaps would blow upward into the atria rather like an umbrella being turned inside out by a strong wind.

The second set of valves, the **pulmonary** and **aortic (semilunar, SL) valves,** each composed of three pocketlike cusps, guards the bases of the two large arteries leaving the ventricular chambers. The valve cusps are forced open and flatten against the walls of the artery as the ventricles discharge their blood into the large arteries during systole. However, when the ventricles relax, blood flows backward toward the heart and the cusps fill with blood, closing the semilunar valves and preventing arterial blood from reentering the heart.

ACTIVITY 1

Using the Heart Model to Study Heart Anatomy

When you have located in Figure 30.2 all the structures described above, observe the human heart model and laboratory charts and reidentify the same structures without referring to the figure. ▪▪▪

Pulmonary, Systemic, and Cardiac Circulations

Pulmonary and Systemic Circulations

The heart functions as a double pump. The right side serves as the **pulmonary circulation** pump, shunting the carbon dioxide–rich blood entering its chambers to the lungs to unload carbon dioxide and pick up oxygen, and then back to the left side of the heart (Figure 30.4). The function of this circuit is strictly to provide for gas exchange. The second circuit, which carries oxygen-rich blood from the left heart through the body tissues and back to the right side of the heart, is called the **systemic circulation.** It provides the functional blood supply to all body tissues.

ACTIVITY 2

Tracing the Path of Blood Through the Heart

Use colored pencils to trace the pathway of a red blood cell through the heart by adding arrows to the frontal section diagram (Figure 30.2b). Use red arrows for the oxygen-rich blood and blue arrows for the less oxygen-rich blood. ▪▪▪

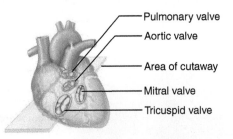

FIGURE 30.3 Heart valves. **(a)** Superior view of the two sets of heart valves (atria removed). **(b)** Photograph of the heart valves, superior view. **(c)** Photograph of the right AV valve. View begins in the right ventricle, looking toward the right atrium. **(d)** Coronal section of the heart.

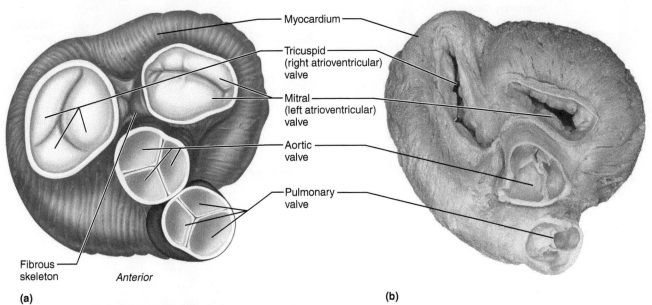

(a)

(b)

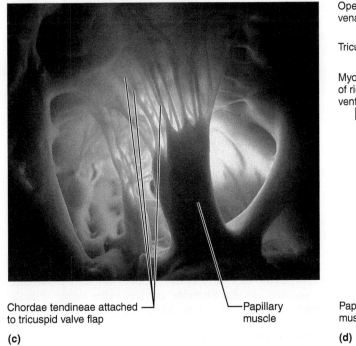

(c)

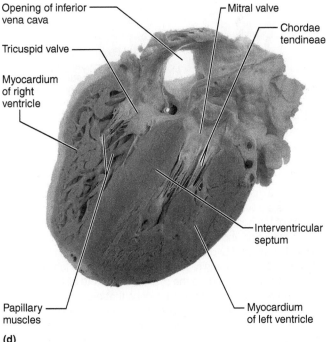

(d)

Coronary Circulation

Even though the heart chambers are almost continually bathed with blood, this contained blood does not nourish the myocardium. The functional blood supply of the heart is provided by the coronary arteries (see Figures 30.2 and 30.5). The **right** and **left coronary arteries** issue from the base of the aorta just above the aortic semilunar valve and encircle the heart in the **coronary sulcus** at the junction of the atria and ventricles. They then ramify over the heart's surface, the right coronary artery supplying the posterior surface of the ventricles and the lateral aspect of the right side of the heart, largely through

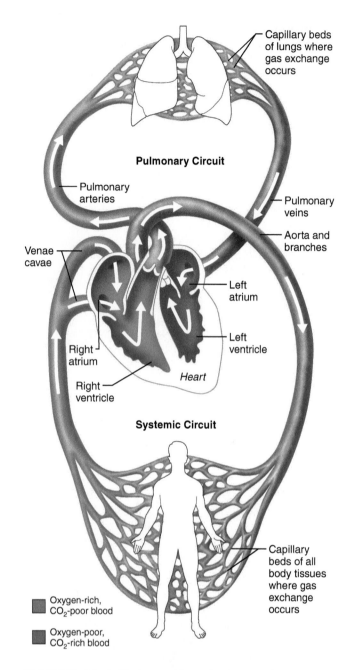

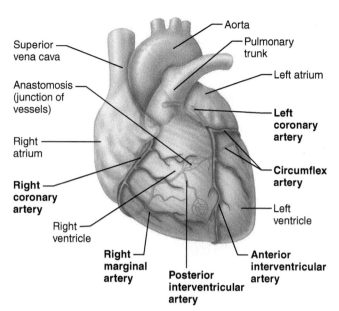

(a) The major coronary arteries

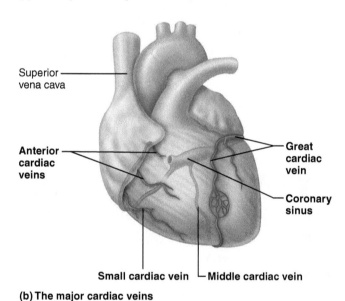

(b) The major cardiac veins

FIGURE 30.5 **Coronary circulation.**

FIGURE 30.4 The systemic and pulmonary circuits.
The heart is a double pump that serves two circulations. The right side of the heart pumps blood through the pulmonary circuit to the lungs and back to the left heart. (For simplicity, the actual number of two pulmonary arteries and four pulmonary veins has been reduced to one each.) The left side of the heart pumps blood via the systemic circuit to all body tissues and back to the right heart. Notice that blood flowing through the pulmonary circuit gains oxygen (O_2) and loses carbon dioxide (CO_2) as depicted by the color change from blue to red. Blood flowing through the systemic circuit loses oxygen and picks up carbon dioxide (red to blue color change).

its **posterior interventricular** and **right marginal artery** branches. The left coronary artery supplies the anterior ventricular walls and the laterodorsal part of the left side of the heart via its two major branches, the **anterior interventricular artery** and the **circumflex artery.** The coronary arteries

and their branches are compressed during systole and fill when the heart is relaxed.

The myocardium is largely drained by the **great, middle, and small cardiac veins,** which empty into the **coronary sinus.** The coronary sinus, in turn, empties into the right atrium. In addition, several **anterior cardiac veins** empty directly into the right atrium (Figure 30.5).

ACTIVITY 3

Using the Heart Model to Study Cardiac Circulation

1. Obtain a highlighter and highlight all the cardiac blood vessels in Figure 30.2a and c. Note how arteries and veins travel together.

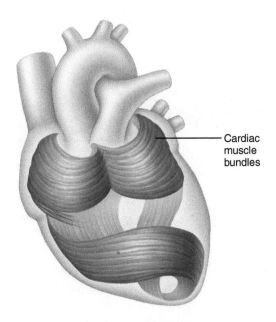

FIGURE 30.6 The circular and spiral arrangement of cardiac muscle bundles in the myocardium.

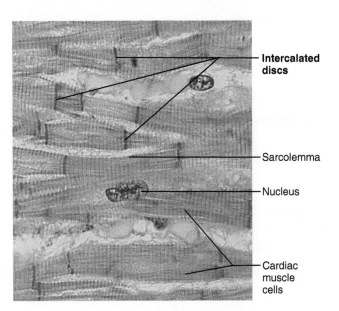

FIGURE 30.7 Photomicrograph of cardiac muscle (570×).

2. On a model of the heart, locate all the cardiac blood vessels shown in Figure 30.5. Use your finger to trace the pathway of blood from the right coronary artery to the lateral aspect of the right side of the heart and back to the right atrium. Name the arteries and veins along the pathway. Trace the pathway of blood from the left coronary artery to the anterior ventricular walls and back to the right atrium. Name the arteries and veins along the pathway. Note that there are multiple different pathways to distribute blood to these parts of the heart. ▬

Microscopic Anatomy of Cardiac Muscle

Cardiac muscle is found in only one place—the heart. The heart acts as a vascular pump, propelling blood to all tissues of the body; cardiac muscle is thus very important to life. Cardiac muscle is involuntary, ensuring a constant blood supply.

The cardiac cells, only sparingly invested in connective tissue, are arranged in spiral or figure-8-shaped bundles (Figure 30.6). When the heart contracts, its internal chambers become smaller (or are temporarily obliterated), forcing the blood into the large arteries leaving the heart.

ACTIVITY 4

Examining Cardiac Muscle Tissue Anatomy

1. Observe the three-dimensional model of cardiac muscle, examining its branching cells and the areas where the cells interdigitate, the **intercalated discs.** These two structural features provide a continuity to cardiac muscle not seen in other muscle tissues and allow close coordination of heart activity.

2. Compare the model of cardiac muscle to the model of skeletal muscle. Note the similarities and differences between the two kinds of muscle tissue.

3. Obtain and observe a longitudinal section of cardiac muscle under high power. Identify the nucleus, striations, intercalated discs, and sarcolemma of the individual cells and then compare your observations to the view seen in Figure 30.7. ▬

DISSECTION:

The Sheep Heart

Dissection of a sheep heart is valuable because it is similar in size and structure to the human heart. Also, a dissection experience allows you to view structures in a way not possible with models and diagrams. Refer to Figure 30.8 as you proceed with the dissection.

1. Obtain a preserved sheep heart, a dissecting tray, dissecting instruments, a glass probe, a plastic ruler, and gloves. Rinse the sheep heart in cold water to remove excessive preservatives and to flush out any trapped blood clots. Now you are ready to make your observations.

2. Observe the texture of the pericardium. Also, note its point of attachment to the heart. Where is it attached?

_____

3. If the serous pericardial sac is still intact, slit open the parietal pericardium and cut it from its attachments. Observe the visceral pericardium (epicardium). Using a sharp scalpel, carefully pull a little of this serous membrane away from the myocardium. How do its position, thickness, and apposition to the heart differ from those of the parietal pericardium?

_____

_____

_____

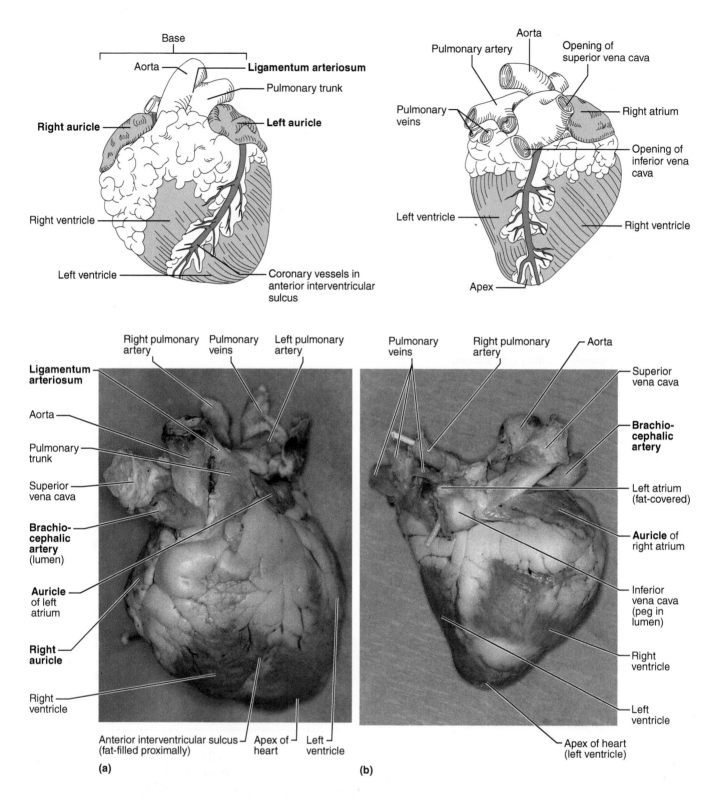

FIGURE 30.8 Anatomy of the sheep heart. (a) Anterior view. **(b)** Posterior view. Diagrammatic views at top; photographs at bottom.

4.   Examine the external surface of the heart. Notice the accumulation of adipose tissue, which in many cases marks the separation of the chambers and the location of the coronary arteries that nourish the myocardium. Carefully scrape away some of the fat with a scalpel to expose the coronary blood vessels.

5.   Identify the base and apex of the heart, and then identify the two wrinkled **auricles,** earlike flaps of tissue projecting from the atrial chambers. The balance of the heart muscle is ventricular tissue. To identify the left ventricle, compress the ventricular chambers on each side of the longitudinal fissures carrying the coronary blood vessels. The side that feels

thicker and more solid is the left ventricle. The right ventricle feels much thinner and somewhat flabby when compressed. This difference reflects the greater demand placed on the left ventricle, which must pump blood through the much longer systemic circulation, a pathway with much higher resistance than the pulmonary circulation served by the right ventricle. Hold the heart in its anatomical position (Figure 30.8a), with the anterior surface uppermost. In this position the left ventricle composes the entire apex and the left side of the heart.

6. Identify the pulmonary trunk and the aorta extending from the superior aspect of the heart. The pulmonary trunk is more anterior, and you may see its division into the right and left pulmonary arteries if it has not been cut too closely to the heart. The thicker-walled aorta, which branches almost immediately, is located just beneath the pulmonary trunk. The first observable branch of the sheep aorta, the **brachiocephalic artery,** is identifiable unless the aorta has been cut immediately as it leaves the heart. The brachiocephalic artery splits to form the right carotid and subclavian arteries, which supply the right side of the head and right forelimb, respectively.

Gently pull on the aorta with your gloved fingers or forceps to stretch it. Repeat with the vena cava.

Which vessel is easier to stretch? _____

How does the elasticity of each vessel relate to its ability to withstand pressure?

_____

Carefully clear away some of the fat between the pulmonary trunk and the aorta to expose the **ligamentum arteriosum,** a cordlike remnant of the **ductus arteriosus.** (In the fetus, the ductus arteriosus allows blood to pass directly from the pulmonary trunk to the aorta, thus bypassing the nonfunctional fetal lungs.)

7. Cut through the wall of the aorta until you see the aortic (semilunar) valve. Identify the two openings to the coronary arteries just above the valve. Insert a probe into one of these holes to see if you can follow the course of a coronary artery across the heart.

8. Turn the heart to view its posterior surface. The heart will appear as shown in Figure 30.8b. Notice that the right and left ventricles appear equal-sized in this view. Try to identify the four thin-walled pulmonary veins entering the left atrium. Identify the superior and inferior venae cavae entering the right atrium. Because of the way the heart is trimmed, the pulmonary veins and superior vena cava may be very short or missing. If possible, compare the approximate diameter of the superior vena cava with the diameter of the aorta.

Which is larger? _____

Which has thicker walls? _____

Why do you suppose these differences exist?

_____

_____

_____

9. Insert a probe into the superior vena cava, through the right atrium, and out the inferior vena cava. Use scissors to cut along the probe so that you can view the interior of the right atrium. Observe the tricuspid valve.

How many flaps does it have? _____

Pour some water into the right atrium and allow it to flow into the ventricle. *Slowly and gently* squeeze the right ventricle to watch the closing action of this valve. (If you squeeze too vigorously, you'll get a face full of water!) Drain the water from the heart before continuing.

10. Return to the pulmonary trunk and cut through its anterior wall until you can see the pulmonary (semilunar) valve (Figure 30.9). Pour some water into the base of the pulmonary trunk to observe the closing action of this valve. How does its action differ from that of the tricuspid valve?

_____

_____

_____

After observing pulmonary valve action, drain the heart once again. Extend the cut through the pulmonary trunk into the right ventricle. Cut down, around, and up through the tricuspid valve to make the cut continuous with the cut across the right atrium (see Figure 30.9).

11. Reflect the cut edges of the superior vena cava, right atrium, and right ventricle to obtain the view seen in Figure 30.9. Observe the comblike ridges of muscle throughout most of the right atrium. This is called **pectinate muscle** (*pectin* = comb). Identify, on the ventral atrial wall, the large opening of the inferior vena cava and follow it to its external opening with a probe. Notice that the atrial walls in the vicinity of the venae cavae are smooth and lack the roughened appearance (pectinate musculature) of the other regions of the atrial walls. Just below the inferior vena caval opening, identify the opening of the **coronary sinus,** which returns venous blood of the coronary circulation to the right atrium. Nearby, locate an oval depression, the **fossa ovalis,** in the interatrial septum. This depression marks the site of an opening in the fetal heart, the **foramen ovale,** which allows blood to pass from the right to the left atrium, thus bypassing the fetal lungs.

12. Identify the papillary muscles in the right ventricle, and follow their attached chordae tendineae to the flaps of the tricuspid valve. Notice the pitted and ridged appearance (**trabeculae carneae**) of the inner ventricular muscle.

13. Identify the **moderator band** (septomarginal band), a bundle of cardiac muscle fibers connecting the interventricular septum to anterior papillary muscles. It contains a branch of the atrioventricular bundle and helps coordinate contraction of the ventricle.

14. Make a longitudinal incision through the left atrium and continue it into the left ventricle. Notice how much thicker the myocardium of the left ventricle is than that of the right

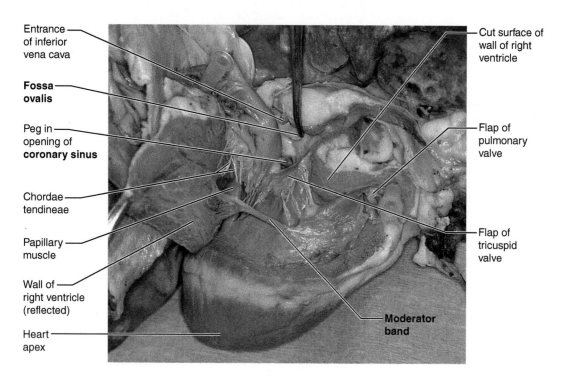

Entrance of inferior vena cava

Fossa ovalis

Peg in opening of **coronary sinus**

Chordae tendineae

Papillary muscle

Wall of right ventricle (reflected)

Heart apex

Cut surface of wall of right ventricle

Flap of pulmonary valve

Flap of tricuspid valve

Moderator band

FIGURE 30.9 Right side of the sheep heart opened and reflected to reveal internal structures.

ventricle. Measure the thickness of right and left ventricular walls and record the numbers.

_____

How do your numbers compare with those of your classmates?

_____

Compare the *shape* of the left ventricular cavity to the shape of the right ventricular cavity. (See Figure 30.10.)

_____

_____

Are the papillary muscles and chordae tendineae observed in

the right ventricle also present in the left ventricle? _____

Count the number of cusps in the mitral valve. How does this compare with the number seen in the tricuspid valve?

_____

How do the sheep valves compare with their human counterparts?

_____

15. Reflect the cut edges of the atrial wall, and attempt to locate the entry points of the pulmonary veins into the left

atrium. Follow the pulmonary veins, if present, to the heart exterior with a probe. Notice how thin-walled these vessels are.

16. Dispose of the organic debris in the designated container, clean the dissecting tray and instruments with detergent and water, and wash the lab bench with bleach solution before leaving the laboratory. ▬

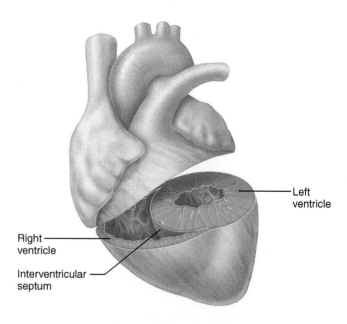

Left ventricle

Right ventricle

Interventricular septum

FIGURE 30.10 Anatomical differences between the right and left ventricles. The left ventricle has thicker walls, and its cavity is basically circular; by contrast, the right ventricle cavity is crescent-shaped and wraps around the left ventricle.

NAME ______________________

LAB TIME/DATE ______________

REVIEW SHEET 30
EXERCISE

Anatomy of the Heart

Gross Anatomy of the Human Heart

1. An anterior view of the heart is shown here. Match each structure listed on the left with the correct letter in the figure.

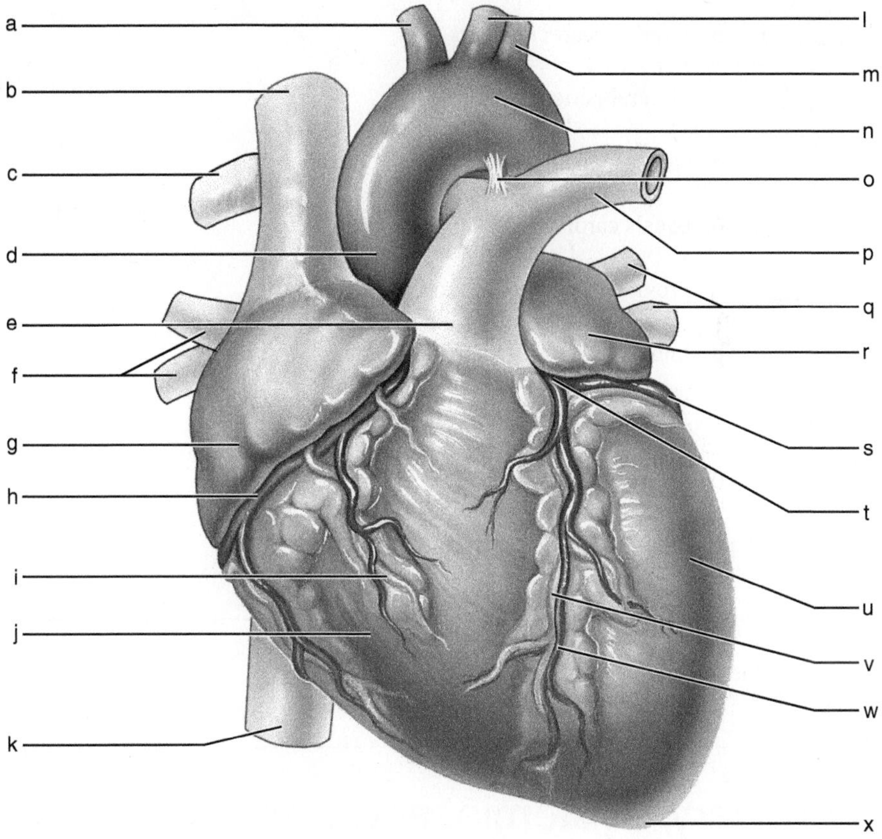

_______ 1. right atrium

_______ 2. right ventricle

_______ 3. left atrium

_______ 4. left ventricle

_______ 5. superior vena cava

_______ 6. inferior vena cava

_______ 7. ascending aorta

_______ 8. aortic arch

_______ 9. brachiocephalic artery

_______ 10. left common carotid artery

_______ 11. left subclavian artery

_______ 12. pulmonary trunk

_______ 13. right pulmonary artery

_______ 14. left pulmonary artery

_______ 15. ligamentum arteriosum

_______ 16. right pulmonary veins

_______ 17. left pulmonary veins

_______ 18. right coronary artery

_______ 19. anterior cardiac vein

_______ 20. left coronary artery

_______ 21. circumflex artery

_______ 22. anterior interventricular artery

_______ 23. apex of heart

_______ 24. great cardiac vein

2. What is the function of the fluid that fills the pericardial sac? _____

_____

3. Match the terms in the key to the descriptions provided below.   *Key:*

       _____   1. location of the heart in the thorax   a.   atria

       _____   2. superior heart chambers   b.   coronary arteries

       _____   3. inferior heart chambers   c.   coronary sinus

       _____   4. visceral pericardium   d.   endocardium

       _____   5. "anterooms" of the heart   e.   epicardium

       _____   6. equals cardiac muscle   f.   mediastinum

       _____   7. provide nutrient blood to the heart muscle   g.   myocardium

       _____   8. lining of the heart chambers   h.   ventricles

       _____   9. actual "pumps" of the heart

       _____ 10. drains blood into the right atrium

4. What is the function of the valves found in the heart? _____

_____

5. What is the role of the chordae tendineae? _____

_____

Pulmonary, Systemic, and Cardiac Circulations

6. A simple schematic of general circulation is shown below. What part of the circulation is missing from this diagram?

_____ Add to the diagram as best you can to make it depict a complete systemic/pulmonary circulation. La-

bel the systemic and pulmonary circulations.

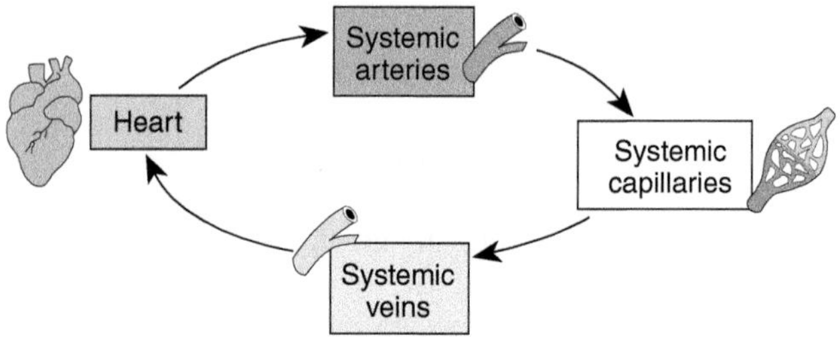

_____   _____

7. Differentiate clearly between the roles of the pulmonary and systemic circulations. _____

_____

_____

8. Complete the following scheme of circulation of a red blood cell in the human body.

Right atrium through the tricuspid valve to the _____, through the _____

valve to the pulmonary trunk, to the _____, to the capillary beds of the lungs, to the _____,

to the _____ of the heart, through the _____ valve to the _____,

through the _____ valve to the _____, to the systemic arteries, to the

_____ of the tissues, to the systemic veins, to the _____, _____,

and _____ entering the right atrium of the heart.

9. If the mitral valve does not close properly, which circulation is affected? _____

10. Why might a thrombus (blood clot) in the anterior descending branch of the left coronary artery cause sudden death?

_____

Microscopic Anatomy of Cardiac Muscle

11. How would you distinguish the structure of cardiac muscle from that of skeletal muscle? _____

_____

_____

12. Add the following terms to the photograph of cardiac muscle below.

   a.   intercalated disc   b.   nucleus of cardiac fiber   c.   striations   d.   cardiac muscle fiber

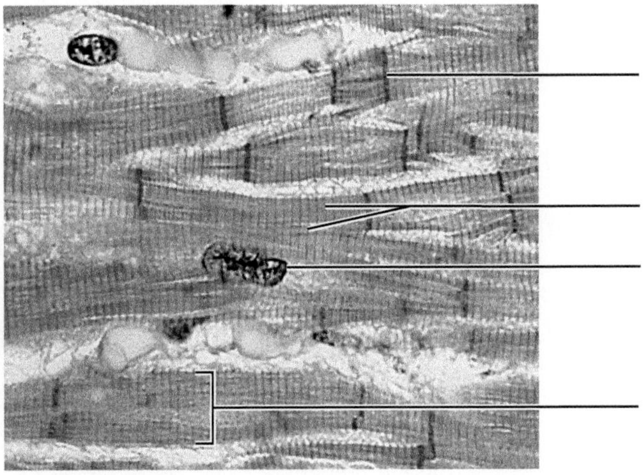

Describe the unique anatomical features of cardiac muscle. What role does the unique structure of cardiac muscle play in its function?

_____

_____

_____

_____

_____

_____

Dissection of the Sheep Heart

13. During the sheep heart dissection, you were asked initially to identify the right and left ventricles without cutting into the heart. During this procedure, what differences did you observe between the two chambers?

_____

_____

When you measured thickness of ventricular walls, was the right or left ventricle thicker? _____

Knowing that structure and function are related, how would you say this structural difference reflects the relative functions

of these two heart chambers? _____

_____

14. Semilunar valves prevent backflow into the _____; mitral and tricuspid valves prevent back-

flow into the _____. Using your own observations, explain how the operation of the semilu-

nar valves differs from that of the mitral and tricuspid valves. _____

_____

_____

_____

15. Compare and contrast the structure of the mitral and tricuspid valves. _____

_____

16. Two remnants of fetal structures are observable in the heart—the ligamentum arteriosum and the fossa ovalis. What were they called in the fetal heart, where was each located, and what common purpose did they serve as functioning fetal structures?

_____

_____

_____

Conduction System of the Heart and Electrocardiography

MATERIALS

☐ Apparatus A or B:*

A: ECG recording apparatus, electrode paste, alcohol swabs, rubber straps or disposable electrodes

BIOPAC B: BIOPAC® MP36 (or MP35/30) data acquisition unit, PC or Mac computer BIOPAC® Student Lab Software, electrode lead set, disposable vinyl electrodes

New versions of the BSL software (3.7.5 and higher for Windows, and 3.7.4 and higher for Mac) require slightly different channel settings and collection strategies. Instructions for using the newer software with the MP36/35 data acquisition units can be found on myA&P. In addition, instructions for use of the **NEW** 2-channel data acquisition unit, the MP45, may also be found on myA&P.

☐ Cot or lab table; pillow (optional)

☐ Millimeter ruler

*Note: Instructions for using PowerLab® equipment can be found on myA&P.

OBJECTIVES

1. To list and localize the elements of the intrinsic conduction, or nodal, system of the heart, and to describe how impulses are initiated and conducted through this system and the myocardium.

2. To interpret the ECG in terms of depolarization and repolarization events occurring in the myocardium; and to identify the P, QRS, and T waves on an ECG recording using an ECG recorder or BIOPAC®.

3. To calculate the heart rate, QRS interval, P–R interval, and Q–T interval from an ECG obtained during the laboratory period.

4. To define *tachycardia, bradycardia,* and *fibrillation.*

PRE-LAB QUIZ

1. Circle True or False. Cardiac muscle cells are electrically connected by gap junctions and behave as a single unit.

2. Because it sets the rate of depolarization for the normal heart, the _____ node is known as the pacemaker of the heart.
   a. atrioventricular
   b. Purkinje
   c. sinoatrial

3. Circle True or False. Activity of the nerves of the autonomic nervous system is essential for cardiac muscle to contract.

4. Today you will create a graphic recording of the electrical changes that occur during a cardiac cycle. This is known as an
   a. electrocardiogram
   b. electroencephalogram
   c. electromyogram

5. Circle the correct term. The typical ECG has three / six normally recognizable deflection waves.

6. In a typical ECG, the _____ wave signals the depolarization of the atria immediately before they contract.
   a. P   c. R
   b. Q   d. T

7. Circle True or False. The repolarization of the atria is usually masked by the large QRS complex.

8. Circle the correct term. A heart rate over 100 beats/minute is known as tachycardia / bradycardia.

9. How many electrodes will you place on your subject for today's activity if using a standard ECG apparatus?
   a. 3   c. 10
   b. 4   d. 12

10. Circle True or False. Electrical activity recorded by any lead depends on the location and orientation of the recording electrodes.

myA&P *For practice quizzes on this lab, go to www.myaandp.com.*

FIGURE 31.1 The intrinsic conduction system of the heart. Dashed-line arrows indicate transmission of the impulse from the SA node through the atria. Solid yellow arrow indicates transmission of the impulse from the SA node to the AV node via the internodal pathway.

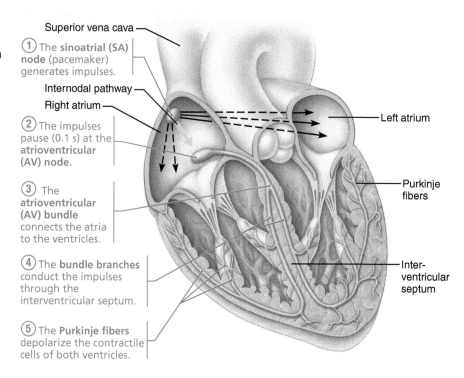

① The **sinoatrial (SA) node** (pacemaker) generates impulses.

② The impulses pause (0.1 s) at the **atrioventricular (AV) node.**

③ The **atrioventricular (AV) bundle** connects the atria to the ventricles.

④ The **bundle branches** conduct the impulses through the interventricular septum.

⑤ The **Purkinje fibers** depolarize the contractile cells of both ventricles.

Superior vena cava

Internodal pathway

Right atrium

Left atrium

Purkinje fibers

Interventricular septum

Heart contraction results from a series of electrical potential changes (depolarization waves) that travel through the heart preliminary to each beat. Because cardiac muscle cells are electrically connected by gap junctions, the entire myocardium behaves like a single unit, a **functional syncytium** (sin-sih′shum).

The Intrinsic Conduction System

The ability of cardiac muscle to beat is intrinsic—it does not depend on impulses from the nervous system to initiate its contraction and will continue to contract rhythmically even if all nerve connections are severed. However, two types of controlling systems exert their effects on heart activity. One of these involves nerves of the autonomic nervous system, which accelerate or decelerate the heartbeat rate depending on which division is activated. The second system is the **intrinsic conduction system,** or **nodal system,** of the heart, consisting of specialized noncontractile myocardial tissue. The intrinsic conduction system ensures that heart muscle depolarizes in an orderly and sequential manner (from atria to ventricles) and that the heart beats as a coordinated unit.

The components of the intrinsic conduction system include the **sinoatrial (SA) node,** located in the right atrium just inferior to the entrance to the superior vena cava; the **atrioventricular (AV) node** in the lower atrial septum at the junction of the atria and ventricles; the **AV bundle (bundle of His)** and right and left **bundle branches,** located in the interventricular septum; and the **Purkinje fibers,** essentially long strands of barrel-shaped cells called *Purkinje myocytes,* which ramify within the muscle bundles of the ventricular

walls. The Purkinje fiber network is much denser and more elaborate in the left ventricle because of the larger size of this chamber (Figure 31.1).

The SA node, which has the highest rate of discharge, provides the stimulus for contraction. Because it sets the rate of depolarization for the heart as a whole, the SA node is often referred to as the *pacemaker.* From the SA node, the impulse spreads throughout the atria and to the AV node. This electrical wave is immediately followed by atrial contraction. At the AV node, the impulse is momentarily delayed (approximately 0.1 sec), allowing the atria to complete their contraction. It then passes through the AV bundle, the right and left bundle branches, and the Purkinje fibers, finally resulting in ventricular contraction. Note that the atria and ventricles are separated from one another by a region of electrically inert connective tissue, so the depolarization wave can be transmitted to the ventricles only via the tract between the AV node and AV bundle. Thus, any damage to the AV node-bundle pathway partially or totally insulates the ventricles from the influence of the SA node. Although autorhythmic cells are found throughout the heart, their rates of spontaneous depolarization differ. The nodal system increases the rate of heart depolarization and synchronizes heart activity.

Electrocardiography

The conduction of impulses through the heart generates electrical currents that eventually spread throughout the body. These impulses can be detected on the body's surface and recorded with an instrument called an *electrocardiograph.* The graphic recording of the electrical changes (depolarization followed by repolarization) occurring during the cardiac cycle is called an **electrocardiogram (ECG or EKG)** (Figure 31.2). For analysis, the ECG is divided into segments and intervals,

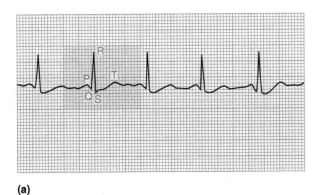

(a)

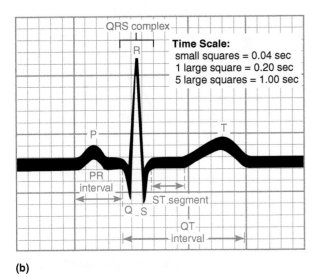

(b)

FIGURE 31.2 The normal electrocardiogram.
(a) Regular sinus rhythm. **(b)** Waves, segments, and intervals of a normal ECG.

TABLE 31.1	Boundaries of Each ECG Component
Feature	**Boundaries**
P wave	Start of P deflection to return to isoelectric line
P–R interval	Start of P deflection to start of Q deflection
P–R segment	End of P wave to start of Q deflection
QRS complex	Start of Q deflection to S return to isoelectric line
S–T segment	End of S deflection to start of T wave
Q–T interval	Start of Q deflection to end of T wave
T wave	Start of T deflection to return to isoelectric line
End T to next R	End of T wave to next R spike

which are defined in Table 31.1. The relationship between the deflection waves of an ECG and sequential excitation of the heart is shown in Figure 31.3.

It is important to understand what an ECG does *and does not* show: First, an ECG is a record of voltage and time—nothing else. Although we can and do infer that muscle contraction follows its excitation, sometimes it does not. Second, an ECG records electrical events occurring in relatively large amounts of muscle tissue (i.e., the bulk of the heart muscle), *not* the activity of nodal tissue which, like muscle contraction, can only be inferred. Nonetheless, abnormalities of the deflection waves and changes in the time intervals of the ECG are useful in detecting myocardial infarcts or problems with the conduction system of the heart. The P–R interval represents the time between the beginning of atrial depolarization and ventricular depolarization. Thus, it typically includes the period during which the depolarization wave passes to the AV node, atrial systole, and

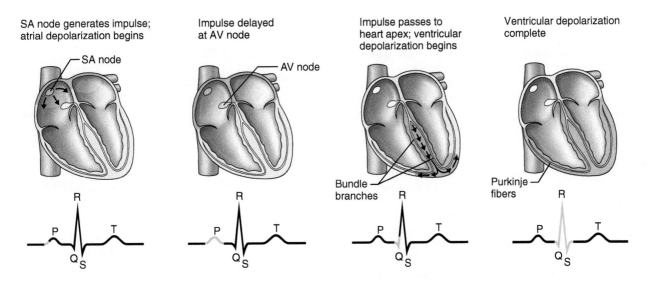

FIGURE 31.3 The sequence of excitation of the heart related to the deflection waves of an ECG tracing.

the passage of the excitation wave to the balance of the conducting system. Generally, the P–R interval is about 0.16 to 0.18 sec. A longer interval may suggest a partial AV heart block caused by damage to the AV node. In total heart block, no impulses are transmitted through the AV node, and the atria and ventricles beat independently of one another—the atria at the SA node rate and the ventricles at their intrinsic rate, which is considerably slower.

A prolonged QRS complex (normally 0.08 sec) may indicate a right or left bundle branch block in which one ventricle is contracting later than the other. The Q–T interval is the period from the beginning of ventricular depolarization through repolarization and includes the time of ventricular contraction (the S–T segment). With a heart rate of 70 beats/min, this interval is normally 0.31 to 0.41 sec. As the rate increases, this interval becomes shorter; conversely, when the heart rate drops, the interval is longer. The repolarization of the atria, which occurs during the QRS interval, is generally obscured by the large QRS complex.

A heart rate over 100 beats/min is referred to as **tachycardia;** a rate below 60 beats/min is **bradycardia.** Although neither condition is pathological, prolonged tachycardia may progress to **fibrillation,** a condition of rapid uncoordinated heart contractions which makes the heart useless as a pump. Bradycardia in athletes is a positive finding; that is, it indicates an increased efficiency of cardiac functioning. Because *stroke volume* (the amount of blood ejected by a ventricle with each contraction) increases with physical conditioning, the heart can contract more slowly and still meet circulatory demands.

Twelve standard leads are used to record an ECG for diagnostic purposes. Three of these are bipolar leads that measure the voltage difference between the arms, or an arm and a leg, and nine are unipolar leads. Together the 12 leads provide a fairly comprehensive picture of the electrical activity of the heart.

For this investigation, four electrodes are used (Figure 31.4), and results are obtained from the three *standard limb leads* (also shown in Figure 31.4). Several types of physiographs or ECG recorders are available. Your instructor will provide specific directions on how to set up and use the available apparatus if standard ECG apparatus is used (Activity 1a). Instructions for use of BIOPAC® apparatus (Activity 1b) are provided on pages 462–466.

Understanding the Standard Limb Leads

As you might expect, electrical activity recorded by any lead depends on the location and orientation of the recording electrodes. Clinically, it is assumed that the heart lies in the center of a triangle with sides of equal lengths (*Einthoven's triangle*) and that the recording connections are made at the vertices (corners) of that triangle. But in practice, the electrodes connected to each arm and to the left leg are considered to connect to the triangle vertices. The standard limb leads record the voltages generated in the extracellular fluids surrounding the heart by the ion flows occurring simultaneously in many cells between any two of the connections. A recording using lead I (RA–LA), which connects the right arm (RA) and the left arm (LA), is most sensitive to electrical activity spreading horizontally across the heart. Lead II (RA–LL) and lead III (LA–LL) record activity along the vertical axis (from the base of the heart to its apex) but from different orientations. The significance of Einthoven's triangle is that the sum of the voltages of leads I and III equals that in lead II (Einthoven's law). Hence, if the voltages of two of the standard leads are recorded, that of the third lead can be determined mathematically.

Once the subject is prepared, the ECG will be recorded first under baseline (resting) conditions and then under conditions of fairly strenuous activity. Finally, recordings will be made while the subject holds his or her breath or carries out deep breathing. The activity recordings and those involving changes in respiratory rate or depth will be compared to the baseline recordings, and you will be asked to determine the reasons for the observed differences in the recordings.

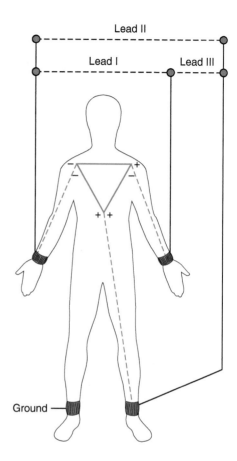

FIGURE 31.4 ECG recording positions for the standard limb leads.

ACTIVITY 1A

Recording ECGs Using a Standard ECG Apparatus

Preparing the Subject

1. If using electrodes that require paste, place electrode paste on four electrode plates and position each electrode as follows after scrubbing the skin at the attachment site with an alcohol swab. Attach an electrode to the anterior surface of each forearm, about 5 to 8 cm (2 to 3 in.) above the wrist, and secure them with rubber straps. In the same manner, attach an electrode to each leg, approximately 5 to 8 cm above the medial malleolus (inner aspect of the ankle). Disposable electrodes may be placed directly on the subject in the same areas.

2. Attach the appropriate tips of the patient cable to the electrodes. The cable leads are marked RA (right arm), LA (left arm), LL (left leg), and RL (right leg, the ground).

Making a Baseline Recording

1. Position the subject comfortably in a supine position on a cot (if available), or sitting relaxed on a laboratory chair.

2.   Turn on the power switch and adjust the sensitivity knob to 1. Set the paper speed to 25 mm/sec and the lead selector to the position corresponding to recording from lead I (RA–LA).

3.   Set the control knob at the **RUN** position and record the subject's at-rest ECG from lead I for 2 to 3 minutes or until the recording stabilizes. (You will need a tracing long enough to provide each student in your group with a representative segment.) The subject should try to relax and not move unnecessarily, because the skeletal muscle action potentials will also be picked up and recorded.

4.   Stop the recording and mark it "lead I."

5.   Repeat the recording procedure for leads II (RA–LL) and III (LA–LL).

6.   Each student should take a representative segment of one of the lead recordings and label the record with the name of the subject and the lead used. Identify and label the P, QRS, and T waves. The calculations you perform for your recording should be based on the following information: Because the paper speed was 25 mm/sec, each millimeter of paper corresponds to a time interval of 0.04 sec. Thus, if an interval requires 4 mm of paper, its duration is 4 mm $\times$ 0.04 sec/mm = 0.16 sec.

7.   Compute the heart rate. Obtain a millimeter ruler and measure the distance from the beginning of one QRS complex to the beginning of the next QRS complex. Enter this value into the following equation to find the time for one heartbeat.

_____ mm/beat $\times$ 0.04 sec/mm = _____ sec/beat

Now find the beats per minute, or heart rate, by using the figure just computed for seconds per beat in the following equation:

$$\frac{1}{\underline{\qquad} \text{ sec/beat}} \times 60 \text{ sec/min} = \underline{\qquad} \text{ beats/min}$$

Is the obtained value within normal limits?_____

Measure the QRS complex, and compute its duration.

_____

Measure the Q–T interval, and compute its duration.

_____

Measure the P–R interval, and compute its duration.

_____

Are the computed values within normal limits?

_____

8.   At the bottom of this page, attach segments of the ECG recordings from leads I through III. Make sure you indicate the paper speed, lead, and subject's name on each tracing. To the recording on which you based your previous computations, add your calculations for the duration of the QRS complex and the P–R and Q–T intervals above the respective area of tracing. Also record the heart rate on that tracing.

Recording the ECG for Running in Place

1.   Make sure the electrodes are securely attached to prevent electrode movement while recording the ECG.

2.   Set the paper speed to 25 mm/sec, and prepare to make the recording using lead I.

3.   Record the ECG while the subject is running in place for 3 minutes. Then have the subject sit down, but continue to record the ECG for an additional 4 minutes. *Mark the recording* at the end of the 3 minutes of running and at 1 minute after cessation of activity.

4.   Stop the recording. Compute the beats/min during the third minute of running, at 1 minute after exercise, and at 4 minutes after exercise. Record below:

_____ beats/min while running in place

_____ beats/min at 1 minute after exercise

_____ beats/min at 4 minutes after exercise

5.   Compare this recording with the previous recording from lead I. Which intervals are shorter in the "running" recording?

_____

Does the subject's heart rate return to resting level by 4 minutes after exercise?

_____

Recording the ECG During Breath Holding

1.   Position the subject comfortably in the sitting position.

2.   Using lead I and a paper speed of 25 mm/sec, begin the recording. After approximately 10 seconds, instruct the subject to begin breath holding and mark the record to indicate the onset of the 1-minute breath-holding interval.

3.   Stop the recording after 1 minute and remind the subject to breathe. Compute the beats/minute during the 1-minute experimental (breath-holding) period.

Beats/min during breath holding: _____

4.   Compare this recording with the lead I recording obtained under resting conditions.

What differences are seen? _____

_____

Attempt to explain the physiological reason for the differences you have seen. (Hint: A good place to start might be to check hypoventilation or the role of the respiratory system in acid-base balance of the blood.)

_____

_____

_____

_____

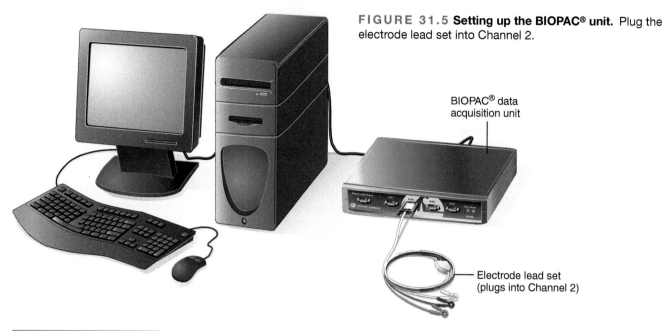

FIGURE 31.5 **Setting up the BIOPAC® unit.** Plug the electrode lead set into Channel 2.

BIOPAC® data acquisition unit

Electrode lead set (plugs into Channel 2)

ACTIVITY 1B

Electrocardiography Using BIOPAC®

In this activity, you will record the electrical activity of the heart under three different conditions: (1) while the subject is lying down, (2) after the subject sits up and breathes normally, and (3) after the subject has exercised and is breathing deeply.

Since the electrodes are not placed directly over the heart, artifacts can result from the recording of unwanted skeletal muscle activity. In order to obtain a clear ECG, it is important that the subject:

- Remain still during the recording.

- Refrain from laughing or talking during the recording.

- When in the sitting position, keep arms and legs steady and relaxed.

Setting Up the Equipment

1. Connect the BIOPAC® unit to the computer and turn the computer **ON.**

2. Make sure the BIOPAC® unit is **OFF.**

3. Plug in the equipment as shown in Figure 31.5:

- Electrode lead set—CH 2

4. Turn the BIOPAC® unit **ON.**

5. Place the three electrodes on the subject as shown in Figure 31.6, and attach the electrode leads according to the colors indicated. The electrodes should be placed on the medial surface of each leg, 5 to 8 cm (2 to 3 in.) superior to the ankle. The other electrode should be placed on the right anterior forearm 5 to 8 cm above the wrist.

6. The subject should lie down and relax in a comfortable position. A chair or place to sit up should be available nearby.

7. Start the BIOPAC® Student Lab program on the computer by double-clicking the icon on the desktop or by following your instructor's guidance.

8. Select lesson **L05-ECG-1** from the menu, and click **OK.**

9. Type in a filename that will save this subject's data on the computer hard drive. You may want to use the subject's last name followed by ECG-1 (for example, SmithECG-1), then click **OK.**

Calibrating the Equipment

- Examine the electrodes and the electrode leads to be certain they are properly attached.

1. The subject must remain still and relaxed. With the subject in a still position, click **Calibrate.** This will initiate the process whereby the computer will automatically establish parameters to record the data.

2. The calibration procedure will stop automatically after 8 seconds.

3. Observe the recording of the calibration data, which should look similar to the data in Figure 31.7.

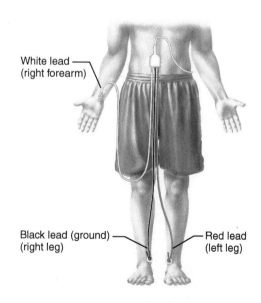

White lead (right forearm)

Black lead (ground) (right leg)

Red lead (left leg)

FIGURE 31.6 **Placement of electrodes and the appropriate attachment of electrode leads by color.**

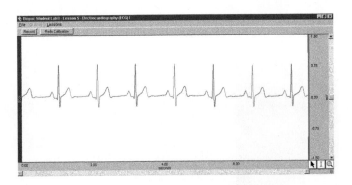

FIGURE 31.7 Example of calibration data.

- If the data look very different, click **Redo Calibration** and repeat the steps above.

- If the data look similar, proceed to the next section.

Recording Segment 1: Subject Lying Down

1. To prepare for the recording, remind the subject to remain still and relaxed while lying down.

2. When prepared, click **Record** and gather data for 20 seconds. At the end of 20 seconds, click **Suspend.**

3. Observe the data, which should look similar to the data in Figure 31.8.

- If the data look very different, click **Redo** and repeat the steps above. Be certain to check attachment of the electrodes and leads, and remind the subject not to move, talk, or laugh.

- If the data look similar, move on to the next recording segment.

Recording Segment 2: After Subject Sits Up, With Normal Breathing

1. Tell the subject to be ready to sit up in the designated location. With the exception of breathing, the subject should try to remain motionless after assuming the seated position. *If the subject moves too much during recording after sitting up, unwanted skeletal muscle artifacts will affect the recording.*

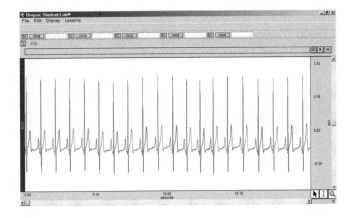

FIGURE 31.8 Example of ECG data while the subject is lying down.

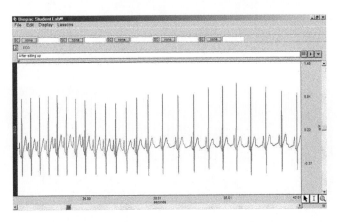

FIGURE 31.9 Example of ECG data after the subject sits up and breathes normally.

2. When prepared, instruct the subject to sit up. Immediately after the subject assumes a motionless state, click **Resume,** and the data will begin recording.

3. At the end of 20 seconds, click **Suspend** to stop recording.

4. Observe the data, which should look similar to the data in Figure 31.9.

- If the data look very different, click **Redo** and repeat the steps above. Be certain to check attachment of the electrodes, and do not click **Resume** until the subject is motionless.

- If the data look similar, move on to the next recording segment. *Note: For start of next segment, ignore the program instructions at the bottom of the computer screen.*

Recording Segment 3: After Subject Exercises, With Deep Breathing

1. Remove the electrode pinch connectors from the electrodes on the subject.

2. Have the subject do a brief round of exercise, such as jumping jacks or running in place for 1 minute, in order to elevate the heart rate.

3. As quickly as possible after the exercise, have the subject resume a motionless, seated position and reattach the pinch connectors. Once again, if the subject moves too much during recording, unwanted skeletal muscle artifacts will affect the data. After exercise, the subject is likely to be breathing deeply, but otherwise should remain as still as possible.

4. Immediately after the subject assumes a motionless, seated state, click **Resume,** and the data will begin recording. Record the ECG for 60 seconds in order to observe postexercise recovery.

5. After 60 seconds, click **Suspend** to stop recording.

6. Observe the data, which should look similar to the data in Figure 31.10.

- If the data look very different, click **Redo** and repeat the steps above. Be certain to check attachment of the electrodes and leads, and remember not to click **Resume** until the subject is motionless.

7. When finished, click **Done.** Remove the electrodes from the subject.

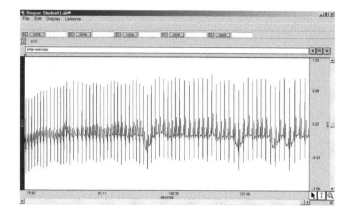

FIGURE 31.10 Example of ECG data after the subject exercises.

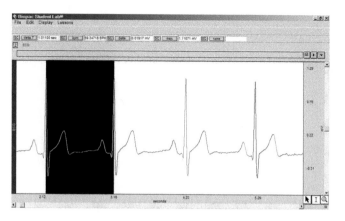

FIGURE 31.11 Example of highlighting from R-wave to R-wave.

8. A pop-up window will appear. To record from another subject, select **Record data from another subject** and return to step 5 under Setting Up the Equipment. If continuing to the Data Analysis section, select **Analyze current data file** and proceed to step 2 of the Data Analysis section.

Data Analysis

1. If just starting the BIOPAC® program to perform data analysis, enter **Review Saved Data** mode and choose the file with the subject's ECG data (for example, SmithECG-1).

2. Use the following tools to adjust the data in order to clearly view and analyze four consecutive cardiac cycles:

• Click the magnifying glass in the lower right corner of the screen (near the I-beam cursor box) to activate the **zoom** function. Use the magnifying glass cursor to click on the very first waveforms until there are about 4 seconds of data represented (see horizontal time scale at the bottom of the screen).

• Select the **Display** menu at the top of the screen, and click **Autoscale Waveforms.** This function will adjust the data for better viewing.

• Click the **Adjust Baseline** button. Two new buttons will appear; simply click these buttons to move the waveforms **Up** or **Down** so they appear clearly in the center of the screen. Once they are centered, click **Exit.**

3. Set up the first two pairs of channel/measurement boxes at the top of the screen by selecting the following channels and measurement types from the drop-down menus (note that Channel 2 contains the ECG data):

Channel	Measurement
CH 2	deltaT
CH 2	bpm

Analysis of Segment 1: Subject Lying Down

1. Use the arrow cursor and click the I-beam cursor box on the lower right side of the screen to activate the "area selection" function.

2. First measure **deltaT** and **bpm** in Segment 1 (approximately seconds 0–20). Using the I-beam cursor, highlight from the peak of one R-wave to the peak of the next R-wave, as shown in Figure 31.11.

3. Observe that the computer automatically calculates the **deltaT** and **bpm** for the selected area. These measurements represent the following:

deltaT (difference in time): Computes the elapsed time between the beginning and end of the highlighted area

bpm (beats per minute): Computes the beats per minute when highlighting from the R-wave of one cycle to the R-wave of another cycle

4. Record this data in the Segment 1 Samples chart below under R to R Sample 1 (round to the nearest 0.01 second and 0.1 beat per minute).

5. Using the I-beam cursor, highlight two other pairs of R to R areas in this segment and record the data in the same chart under Samples 2 and 3.

Segment 1 Samples for deltaT and bpm						
Measure	Channel	R to R Sample 1	R to R Sample 2	R to R Sample 3	Mean	Range
deltaT	CH 2					
bpm	CH 2					

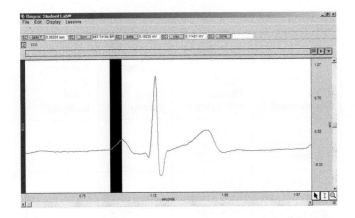

FIGURE 31.12 Example of a single ECG waveform with the first part of the P wave highlighted.

6. Calculate the means and ranges of the data in this chart.

7. Next, use the **zoom, Autoscale Waveforms,** and **Adjust Baseline** tools described above to focus in on one ECG waveform within Segment 1. See the example in Figure 31.12.

8. Once a single ECG waveform is centered for analysis, click the I-beam cursor box on the lower right side of the screen to activate the "area selection" function.

9. Using the highlighting function and **deltaT** computation, measure the duration of every component of the ECG waveform. Refer to Figure 31.2b and Table 31.1 for guidance in highlighting each component.

10. Highlight each component of one cycle. Observe the elapsed time, and record this data under Cycle 1 in the Segment 1 Elapsed Time chart.

11. Scroll along the horizontal axis at the bottom of the data to view and analyze two additional cycles in Segment 1. Record the elapsed time for every component of Cycle 2 and Cycle 3 in the Segment 1 Elapsed Time chart.

12. In the same chart, calculate the means for the three cycles of data and record.

Segment 1 Elapsed Time for ECG Components (seconds)				
Component	Cycle 1	Cycle 2	Cycle 3	Mean
P wave				
P–R interval				
P–R segment				
QRS complex				
S–T segment				
Q–T interval				
T wave				
End T to next R				

Analysis of Segment 2: Subject Sitting Up and Breathing Normally

1. Scroll along the horizontal time bar until you reach the data for Segment 2 (approximately seconds 20–40). A marker with "After sitting up" should denote the beginning of this data.

2. As in the analysis of Segment 1, use the I-beam tool to highlight and measure the **deltaT** and **bpm** between three different pairs of R-waves in this segment, and record the data in the Segment 2 Samples chart below.

Analysis of Segment 3: After Exercise with Deep Breathing

1. Scroll along the horizontal time bar until you reach the data for Segment 3 (approximately seconds 40–60). A marker with "After exercise" should denote the beginning of this data.

Segment 2 Samples for deltaT and bpm						
Measure	Channel	R to R Sample 1	R to R Sample 2	R to R Sample 3	Mean	Range
deltaT	CH 2					
bpm	CH 2					

Segment 3 Samples for deltaT and bpm						
Measure	Channel	R to R Sample 1	R to R Sample 2	R to R Sample 3	Mean	Range
deltaT	CH 2					
bpm	CH 2					

Segment 3 Elapsed Time for ECG Components (seconds)				
Component	Cycle 1	Cycle 2	Cycle 3	Mean
P wave				
P–R interval				
P–R segment				
QRS complex				
S–T segment				
Q–T interval				
T wave				
End T to next R				

Average Duration for ECG Components			
ECG Component	Normal Duration (seconds)	Segment 1 (lying down)	Segment 3 (post-exercise)
P wave	0.06–0.11		
P–R interval	0.12–0.20		
P–R segment	0.08		
QRS complex	Less than 0.12		
S–T segment	0.12		
Q–T interval	0.31–0.41		
T wave	0.16		
End T to next R	varies		

2. As before, use the I-beam tool to highlight and measure the **deltaT** and **bpm** between three pairs of R-waves in this segment, and record the data in the Segment 3 Samples chart on the previous page.

3. Using the instructions for steps 8 and 9 in the section Analysis of Segment 1, highlight and observe the elapsed time for each component of one cycle, and record these data under Cycle 1 in the Segment 3 Elapsed Time chart above.

4. Scroll along the horizontal axis at the bottom of the data to view and analyze two other cycles in Segment 3. Record the elapsed time for each component of Cycle 2 and Cycle 3 in the Segment 3 Elapsed Time chart above.

5. In the same chart, calculate the means for each component in Segment 3.

6. When finished, **Exit** the program.

Compare the average **deltaT** times and average **bpm** between the data in Segment 1 (lying down) and the data in Segment 3 (after exercise). Which is greater in each case?

What is the relationship between elapsed time (**deltaT**) between R-waves and the heart rate?

Is there a change in heart rate when the subject makes the transition from lying down (Segment 1) to a sitting position (Segment 2)?

Examine the average duration of each of the ECG components in Segment 1 and Segment 3. In the chart that follows, record the average values of each component. Draw a circle around those measures that fit within the normal range.

Compare the Q–T intervals in the data while the subject is at rest versus after exercise; this interval corresponds closely to the duration of contraction of the ventricles. Describe and explain any difference.

Compare the duration in the period from the end of each T wave to the next R-spike while the subject is at rest versus after exercise. This interval corresponds closely to the duration of relaxation of the ventricles. Describe and explain any difference.

Which, if any, of the components in the Average Duration chart above demonstrates a significant difference from the normal value? Based on the events of the cardiac cycle and their representation in an ECG, what abnormality might the data suggest?

NAME _____

LAB TIME/DATE _____

Conduction System of the Heart and Electrocardiography

The Intrinsic Conduction System

1. List the elements of the intrinsic conduction system in order, starting from the SA node.

   SA node → _____ → _____ →

   _____ → _____

   At what structure in the transmission sequence is the impulse temporarily delayed? _____

   Why? _____

   _____

2. Even though cardiac muscle has an inherent ability to beat, the nodal system plays a critical role in heart physiology. What

   is that role? _____

   _____

Electrocardiography

3. Define *ECG*. _____

   _____

4. Draw an ECG wave form representing one heartbeat. Label the P, QRS, and T waves; the P–R interval; the S–T segment, and the Q–T interval.

5. Why does heart rate increase during running? _____

   _____

   _____

6. Describe what happens in the cardiac cycle in the following situations.

   1.   immediately before the P wave: _____

   2.   during the P wave: _____

   3.   immediately after the P wave (P–R segment): _____

   4.   during the QRS wave: _____

   5.   immediately after the QRS wave (S–T interval): _____

   6.   during the T wave: _____

7. Define the following terms.

   1.   *tachycardia:* _____

   2.   *bradycardia:* _____

   3.   *fibrillation:* _____

8. Which would be more serious, atrial or ventricular fibrillation? _____

Why? _____

_____

9. Abnormalities of heart valves can be detected more accurately by auscultation than by electrocardiography. Why is this so?

_____

_____

_____

32

Anatomy of Blood Vessels

M A T E R I A L S

☐ Compound microscope
☐ Prepared microscope slides showing cross sections of an artery and vein
☐ Anatomical charts of human arteries and veins (or a three-dimensional model of the human circulatory system)
☐ Anatomical charts of the following specialized circulations: pulmonary circulation, hepatic portal circulation, fetal circulation, arterial supply of the brain (or a brain model showing this circulation)
☐ *Human Cardiovascular System: The Blood Vessels* videotape

✂ For instructions on animal dissections, see the dissection exercises starting on page 697 in the cat, fetal pig, and rat editions of this manual.

O B J E C T I V E S

1. To describe the tunics of blood vessel walls, and to state the function of each layer.
2. To correlate differences in artery, vein, and capillary structure with the functions of these vessels.
3. To recognize a cross-sectional view of an artery and vein when provided with a microscopic view or appropriate diagram.
4. To list and/or identify the major arteries arising from the aorta, and to indicate the body region supplied by each.
5. To list and/or identify the major veins draining into the superior and inferior venae cavae, and to indicate the body regions drained.
6. To point out and/or discuss the unique features of special circulations (pulmonary circulation, hepatic portal system, fetal circulation, cerebral arterial circle [circle of Willis]) in the body.

P R E - L A B   Q U I Z

1. Circle the correct term. <u>Arteries / Veins</u> drain tissues and return blood to the heart.
2. Circle True or False. It is through the walls of capillaries that actual gas exchange takes place between tissue cells and blood.
3. The _____ is the largest artery of the body.
   a. aorta
   b. carotid artery
   c. femoral artery
   d. subclavian artery
4. Circle the correct term. The largest branch of the abdominal aorta, the <u>renal / superior mesenteric</u> artery, supplies most of the small intestine and the first half of the large intestine.
5. The anterior tibial artery terminates with the _____ artery, which is often palpated in patients with circulatory problems to determine the circulatory efficiency of the lower limb.
   a. dorsalis pedis
   b. external iliac
   c. obturator
   d. tibial
6. Circle the correct term. Veins draining the head and upper extremities empty into the <u>superior / inferior</u> vena cava.
7. Located in the lower limb, the _____ is the longest vein in the body.
   a. external iliac
   b. fibular
   c. great saphenous
   d. internal iliac
8. Circle the correct term. The <u>renal / hepatic</u> veins drain the liver.
9. The function of the _____ is to drain the digestive viscera and carry dissolved nutrients to the liver for processing.
   a. fetal circulation
   b. hepatic portal circulation
   c. pulmonary circulation system
10. Circle the correct term. In the developing fetus, the umbilical <u>artery / vein</u> carries blood rich in nutrients and oxygen to the fetus.

myA&P *For practice quizzes on this lab, go to www.myaandp.com.*

PAL *For access to anatomical models and more, check out Practice Anatomy Lab.*

The blood vessels constitute a closed transport system. As the heart contracts, blood is propelled into the large arteries leaving the heart. It moves into successively smaller arteries and then to the arterioles, which feed the capillary beds in the tissues. Capillary beds are drained by the venules, which in turn empty into veins that ultimately converge on the great veins entering the heart.

Arteries, carrying blood away from the heart, and veins, which drain the tissues and return blood to the heart, function simply as conducting vessels or conduits. Only the tiny capillaries that connect the arterioles and venules and ramify throughout the tissues directly serve the needs of the body's cells. It is through the capillary walls that exchanges are made between tissue cells and blood. Respiratory gases, nutrients, and wastes move along diffusion gradients. Thus, oxygen and nutrients diffuse from the blood to the tissue cells, and carbon dioxide and metabolic wastes move from the cells to the blood.

In this exercise you will examine the microscopic structure of blood vessels and identify the major arteries and veins of the systemic circulation and other special circulations.

Microscopic Structure of the Blood Vessels

Except for the microscopic capillaries, the walls of blood vessels are constructed of three coats, or *tunics* (Figure 32.1).

FIGURE 32.1 Generalized structure of arteries, veins, and capillaries. (a) Light photomicrograph of a muscular artery and the corresponding vein in cross section (30×). **(b)** Comparison of wall structure of arteries, veins, and capillaries. Note that the tunica media is thick in arteries and thin in veins, while the tunica externa is thin in arteries and relatively thicker in veins. Capillaries have only endothelium and a sparse basal lamina.

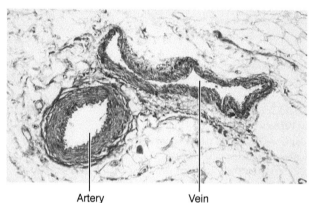

Artery   Vein

(a)

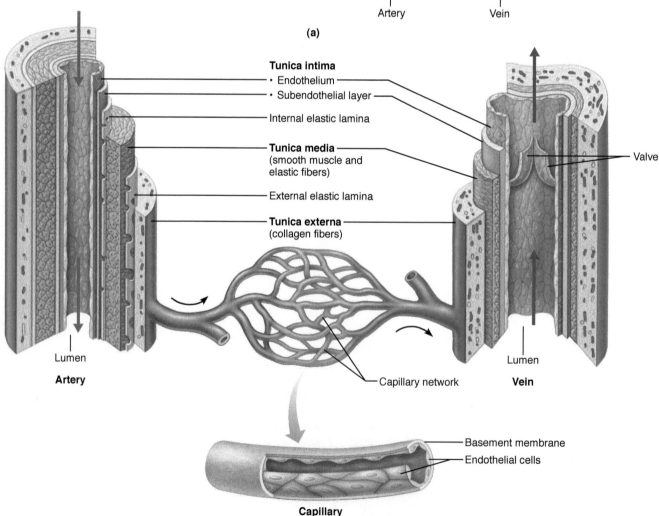

Tunica intima
· Endothelium
· Subendothelial layer
Internal elastic lamina

Tunica media
(smooth muscle and
elastic fibers)

External elastic lamina

Tunica externa
(collagen fibers)

Valve

Lumen

Artery

Lumen

Vein

Capillary network

Basement membrane
Endothelial cells

Capillary

(b)

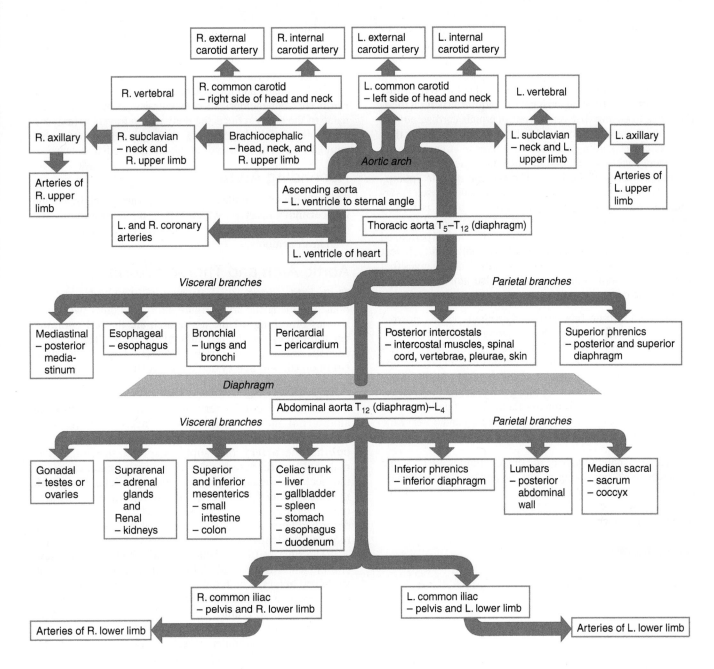

FIGURE 32.2 Schematic of the systemic arterial circulation. (R. = right, L. = left)

The **tunica intima,** or **interna,** which lines the lumen of a vessel, is a single thin layer of *endothelium* (squamous cells underlain by a scant basal lamina) that is continuous with the endocardium of the heart. Its cells fit closely together, forming an extremely smooth blood vessel lining that helps decrease resistance to blood flow.

The **tunica media** is the more bulky middle coat and is composed primarily of smooth muscle and elastin. The smooth muscle, under the control of the sympathetic nervous system, plays an active role in regulating the diameter of blood vessels, which in turn alters peripheral resistance and blood pressure.

The **tunica externa,** or **adventitia,** the outermost tunic, is composed of areolar or fibrous connective tissue. Its function is basically supportive and protective.

In general, the walls of arteries are thicker than those of veins. The tunica media in particular tends to be much heav-

ier and contains substantially more smooth muscle and elastic tissue. This anatomical difference reflects a functional difference in the two types of vessels. Arteries, which are closer to the pumping action of the heart, must be able to expand as an increased volume of blood is propelled into them during systole and then recoil passively as the blood flows off into the circulation during diastole. Their walls must be sufficiently strong and resilient to withstand such pressure fluctuations. Since these larger arteries have such large amounts of elastic tissue in their media, they are often referred to as *elastic arteries.* Smaller arteries, further along in the circulatory pathway, are exposed to less extreme pressure fluctuations. They have less elastic tissue but still have substantial amounts of smooth muscle in their media. For this reason, they are called *muscular arteries.* A schematic of the systemic arteries is provided in Figure 32.2.

By contrast, veins, which are far removed from the heart in the circulatory pathway, are not subjected to such pressure fluctuations and are essentially low-pressure vessels. Thus, veins may be thinner-walled without jeopardy. However, the low-pressure condition itself and the fact that blood returning to the heart often flows against gravity require structural modifications to ensure that venous return equals cardiac output. Thus, the lumens of veins tend to be substantially larger than those of corresponding arteries, and valves in larger veins act to prevent backflow of blood in much the same manner as the semilunar valves of the heart. The skeletal muscle "pump" also promotes venous return; as the skeletal muscles surrounding the veins contract and relax, the blood is milked through the veins toward the heart. (Anyone who has been standing relatively still for an extended time has experienced swelling in the ankles, caused by blood pooling in their feet during the period of muscle inactivity.) Pressure changes that occur in the thorax during breathing also aid the return of blood to the heart.

• To demonstrate how efficiently venous valves prevent backflow of blood, perform the following simple experiment. Allow one hand to hang by your side until the blood vessels on the dorsal aspect become distended. Place two fingertips against one of the distended veins and, pressing firmly, move the superior finger proximally along the vein and then release this finger. The vein will remain flattened and collapsed despite gravity. Then remove the distal fingertip and observe the rapid filling of the vein.

The transparent walls of the tiny capillaries are only one cell layer thick, consisting of just the endothelium underlain by a basal lamina, that is, the tunica intima. Because of this exceptional thinness, exchanges are easily made between the blood and tissue cells.

ACTIVITY 1

Examining the Microscopic Structure of Arteries and Veins

1. Obtain a slide showing a cross-sectional view of blood vessels and a microscope.

2. Using Figure 32.1 as a guide, scan the section to identify a thick-walled artery. Very often, but not always, its lumen will appear scalloped due to the constriction of its walls by the elastic tissue of the media.

3. Identify a vein. Its lumen may be elongated or irregularly shaped and collapsed, and its walls will be considerably thinner. Notice the difference in the relative amount of elastic fibers in the media of the two vessels. Also, note the thinness of the intima layer, which is composed of flat squamous-type cells. ■

Major Systemic Arteries of the Body

The **aorta** is the largest artery of the body. Extending upward as the ascending aorta from the left ventricle, it arches posteriorly and to the left (aortic arch) and then courses downward as the descending aorta through the thoracic cavity. It penetrates the diaphragm to enter the abdominal cavity just anterior to the vertebral column.

Figure 32.2 depicts the relationship of the aorta and its major branches. As you locate the arteries on the figure and other anatomical charts and models, be aware of ways in which you can make your memorization task easier. In many cases the name of the artery reflects the body region traversed (axillary, subclavian, brachial, popliteal), the organ served (renal, hepatic), or the bone followed (tibial, femoral, radial, ulnar).

Ascending Aorta

The only branches of the ascending aorta are the **right** and the **left coronary arteries,** which supply the myocardium. The coronary arteries are described in Exercise 30 in conjunction with heart anatomy.

Aortic Arch and Thoracic Aorta

The **brachiocephalic** (literally, "arm-head") **trunk** is the first branch of the aortic arch (Figure 32.3). The other two major arteries branching off the aortic arch are the **left common carotid artery** and the **left subclavian artery.** The brachiocephalic artery persists briefly before dividing into the **right common carotid artery** and the **right subclavian artery.**

Arteries Serving the Head and Neck

The common carotid artery on each side divides to form an **internal** and an external **carotid artery.** The **internal carotid artery** serves the brain and gives rise to the **ophthalmic artery** that supplies orbital structures. The **external carotid artery** supplies the extracranial tissues of the neck and head, largely via its **superficial temporal, maxillary, facial,** and **occipital** arterial branches. (Notice that several arteries are shown in the figure that are not described here. Ask your instructor which arteries you are required to identify.)

The right and left subclavian arteries each give off several branches to the head and neck. The first of these is the **vertebral artery,** which runs up the posterior neck to supply the cerebellum, part of the brain stem, and the posterior cerebral hemispheres. Issuing just lateral to the vertebral artery are the **thyrocervical trunk,** which mainly serves the thyroid gland and some scapular muscles, and the **costocervical trunk,** which supplies deep neck muscles and some of the upper intercostal muscles. In the armpit, the subclavian artery becomes the axillary artery, which serves the upper limb.

Arteries Serving the Brain

A continuous blood supply to the brain is crucial because oxygen deprivation for even a few minutes causes irreparable damage to the delicate brain tissue. The brain is supplied by two pairs of arteries arising from the region of the aortic arch—the internal carotid arteries and the vertebral arteries. Figure 32.3a is a diagram of the brain's arterial supply.

Within the cranium, each internal carotid artery divides into **anterior** and **middle cerebral arteries,** which supply the bulk of the cerebrum. The right and left anterior cerebral arteries are connected by a short shunt called the **anterior communicating artery.** This shunt, along with shunts from each of the middle cerebral arteries, called the **posterior communicating arteries,** contribute to the formation of the **cerebral arterial circle (circle of Willis),** an arterial anastomosis at the base of the brain surrounding the pituitary gland and the optic chiasma.

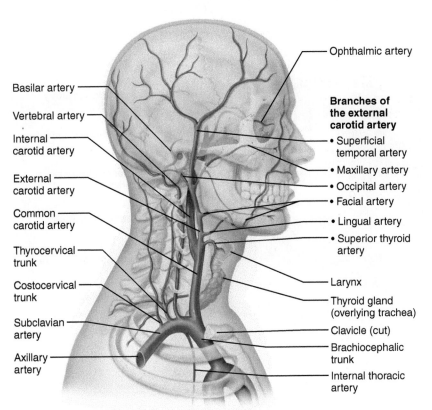

Basilar artery

Vertebral artery

Internal carotid artery

External carotid artery

Common carotid artery

Thyrocervical trunk

Costocervical trunk

Subclavian artery

Axillary artery

Ophthalmic artery

Branches of the external carotid artery

• Superficial temporal artery
• Maxillary artery
• Occipital artery
• Facial artery
• Lingual artery
• Superior thyroid artery

Larynx

Thyroid gland (overlying trachea)

Clavicle (cut)

Brachiocephalic trunk

Internal thoracic artery

(a)

FIGURE 32.3 Arteries of the head, neck, and brain. (a) Right aspect. **(b)** Drawing of the cerebral arteries. Cerebellum is not shown on the left side of the figure. **(c)** Cerebral arterial circle (circle of Willis) in a human brain.

Anterior

Frontal lobe

Olfactory bulb

Optic chiasma

Middle cerebral artery

Internal carotid artery

Pituitary gland

Temporal lobe

Pons

Occipital lobe

Vertebral artery

Posterior

(b)

Cerebral arterial circle (circle of Willis)

• Anterior communicating artery
• Anterior cerebral artery
• Posterior communicating artery
• Posterior cerebral artery
• Basilar artery

Cerebellum

(c)

The paired **vertebral arteries** diverge from the subclavian arteries and pass superiorly through the foramina of the transverse process of the cervical vertebrae to enter the skull through the foramen magnum. Within the skull, the vertebral arteries unite to form a single **basilar artery,** which continues superiorly along the ventral aspect of the brain stem, giving off branches to the pons, cerebellum, and inner ear. At the

base of the cerebrum, the basilar artery divides to form the posterior cerebral arteries. These supply portions of the temporal and occipital lobes of the cerebrum and complete the cerebral arterial circle posteriorly.

The uniting of the blood supply of the internal carotid arteries and the vertebral arteries via the cerebral arterial circle is a protective device that theoretically provides an alternative

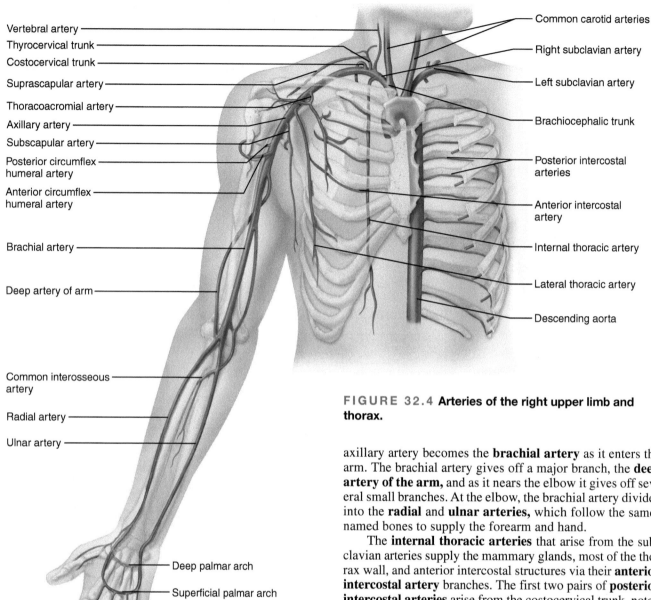

Vertebral artery
Thyrocervical trunk
Costocervical trunk
Suprascapular artery
Thoracoacromial artery
Axillary artery
Subscapular artery
Posterior circumflex humeral artery
Anterior circumflex humeral artery
Brachial artery
Deep artery of arm
Common interosseous artery
Radial artery
Ulnar artery

Common carotid arteries
Right subclavian artery
Left subclavian artery
Brachiocephalic trunk
Posterior intercostal arteries
Anterior intercostal artery
Internal thoracic artery
Lateral thoracic artery
Descending aorta

Deep palmar arch
Superficial palmar arch
Digital arteries

FIGURE 32.4 Arteries of the right upper limb and thorax.

axillary artery becomes the **brachial artery** as it enters the arm. The brachial artery gives off a major branch, the **deep artery of the arm,** and as it nears the elbow it gives off several small branches. At the elbow, the brachial artery divides into the **radial and ulnar arteries,** which follow the same-named bones to supply the forearm and hand.

The **internal thoracic arteries** that arise from the subclavian arteries supply the mammary glands, most of the thorax wall, and anterior intercostal structures via their **anterior intercostal artery** branches. The first two pairs of **posterior intercostal arteries** arise from the costocervical trunk, noted above. The more inferior pairs arise from the thoracic aorta. Not shown in Figure 32.4 are the small arteries that serve the diaphragm *(phrenic arteries),* esophagus *(esophageal arteries),* bronchi *(bronchial arteries),* and other structures of the mediastinum *(mediastinal and pericardial arteries).*

Abdominal Aorta

Although several small branches of the descending aorta serve the thorax (see the previous section), the more major branches of the descending aorta are those serving the abdominal organs and ultimately the lower limbs (Figure 32.5).

Arteries Serving Abdominal Organs

The **celiac trunk** (Figure 32.5a) is an unpaired artery that subdivides almost immediately into three branches: the **left gastric artery** supplying the stomach, the **splenic artery** supplying the spleen, and the **common hepatic artery,** which runs superiorly and gives off branches to the stomach (**right gastric artery**), duodenum, and pancreas. Where the **gastroduodenal artery** branches off, the common hepatic artery becomes the **hepatic artery proper,** which serves the liver. The **right** and **left gastroepiploic arteries,** branches of

set of pathways for blood to reach the brain tissue in the case of arterial occlusion or impaired blood flow anywhere in the system. In actuality, the communicating arteries are tiny, and in many cases the communicating system is defective.

Arteries Serving the Thorax and Upper Limbs

As the **axillary artery** runs through the axilla, it gives off several branches to the chest wall and shoulder girdle (Figure 32.4). These include the **thoracoacromial artery** (to shoulder and pectoral region), the **lateral thoracic artery** (lateral chest wall), the **subscapular artery** (to scapula and dorsal thorax), and the **anterior** and **posterior circumflex humeral arteries** (to the shoulder and the deltoid muscle). At the inferior edge of the teres major muscle, the

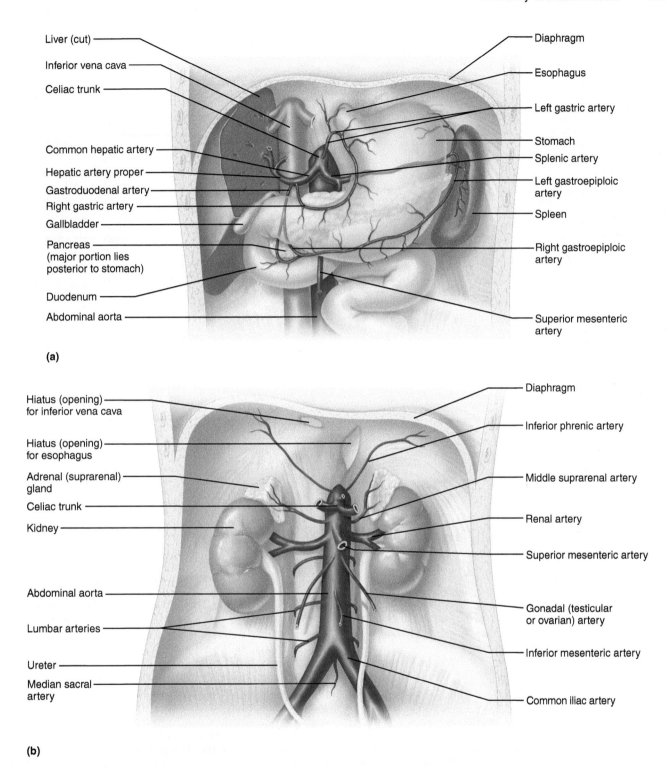

Liver (cut)
Inferior vena cava
Celiac trunk
Common hepatic artery
Hepatic artery proper
Gastroduodenal artery
Right gastric artery
Gallbladder
Pancreas
(major portion lies
posterior to stomach)
Duodenum
Abdominal aorta

Diaphragm
Esophagus
Left gastric artery
Stomach
Splenic artery
Left gastroepiploic
artery
Spleen
Right gastroepiploic
artery
Superior mesenteric
artery

(a)

Hiatus (opening)
for inferior vena cava
Hiatus (opening)
for esophagus
Adrenal (suprarenal)
gland
Celiac trunk
Kidney
Abdominal aorta
Lumbar arteries
Ureter
Median sacral
artery

Diaphragm
Inferior phrenic artery
Middle suprarenal artery
Renal artery
Superior mesenteric artery
Gonadal (testicular
or ovarian) artery
Inferior mesenteric artery
Common iliac artery

(b)

FIGURE 32.5 Arteries of the abdomen. (a) The celiac trunk and its major branches.
(b) Major branches of the abdominal aorta.

the gastroduodenal and splenic arteries respectively, serve the left (greater) curvature of the stomach.

The largest branch of the abdominal aorta, the **superior mesenteric artery** (Figure 32.5b and 32.5c), supplies most of the small intestine (via the intestinal arteries) and the first half of the large intestine (via the ileocolic and colic arteries). Flanking the superior mesenteric artery on the left and right are the **middle suprarenal arteries** serving the adrenal glands that sit atop the kidneys.

The paired **renal arteries** (Figure 32.5b) supply the kidneys, and the **gonadal arteries,** arising from the ventral aortic surface just below the renal arteries, run inferiorly to serve the gonads. They are called **ovarian arteries** in the female and **testicular arteries** in the male. Since these vessels must travel through the inguinal canal to supply the testes, they are considerably longer in the male than the female.

The final major branch of the abdominal aorta is the **inferior mesenteric artery** (Figure 32.5b and 32.5c), which

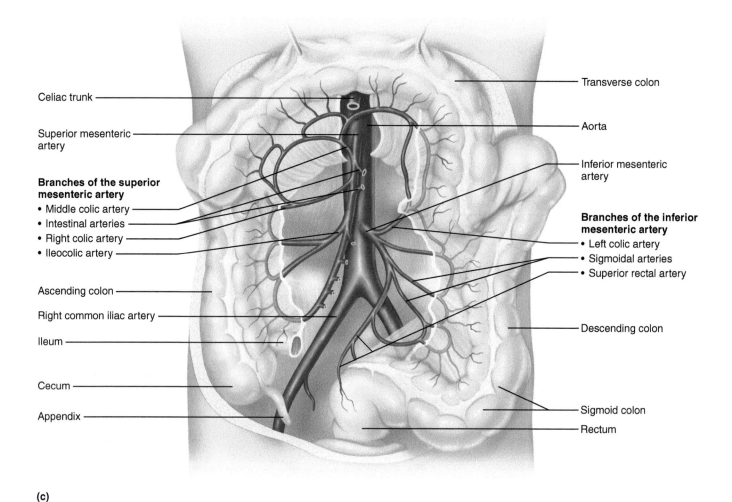

Celiac trunk

Superior mesenteric artery

Branches of the superior mesenteric artery
• Middle colic artery
• Intestinal arteries
• Right colic artery
• Ileocolic artery

Ascending colon

Right common iliac artery

Ileum

Cecum

Appendix

Transverse colon

Aorta

Inferior mesenteric artery

Branches of the inferior mesenteric artery
• Left colic artery
• Sigmoidal arteries
• Superior rectal artery

Descending colon

Sigmoid colon

Rectum

(c)

FIGURE 32.5 *(continued)* **Arteries of the abdomen. (c)** Distribution of the superior and inferior mesenteric arteries, transverse colon pulled superiorly.

supplies the distal half of the large intestine via several branches. Just below this, four pairs of **lumbar arteries** arise from the posterolateral surface of the aorta to supply the posterior abdominal wall (lumbar region).

In the pelvic region, the descending aorta divides into the two large **common iliac arteries,** which serve the pelvis, lower abdominal wall, and the lower limbs.

Arteries Serving the Lower Limbs

Each of the common iliac arteries extends for about 5 cm (2 inches) into the pelvis before it divides into the internal and external iliac arteries (Figure 32.6). The **internal iliac artery** supplies the gluteal muscles via the **superior** and **inferior gluteal arteries** and the adductor muscles of the medial thigh via the **obturator artery,** as well as the external genitalia and perineum (via the *internal pudendal artery,* not illustrated).

The **external iliac artery** supplies the anterior abdominal wall and the lower limb. As it continues into the thigh, its name changes to **femoral artery.** Proximal branches of the femoral artery, the **circumflex femoral arteries,** supply the head and neck of the femur and the hamstring muscles. The femoral artery gives off a deep branch, the **deep artery of the thigh** (also called the **deep femoral artery**), which is the main supply to the thigh muscles (hamstrings, quadriceps, and adductors). In

the knee region, the femoral artery briefly becomes the **popliteal artery;** its subdivisions—the **anterior** and **posterior tibial arteries**—supply the leg, ankle, and foot. The posterior tibial, which supplies flexor muscles, gives off one main branch, the **fibular artery,** that serves the lateral calf (fibular muscles), and then divides into the **lateral** and **medial plantar arteries** that supply blood to the sole of the foot. The anterior tibial artery supplies the extensor muscles and terminates with the **dorsalis pedis artery.** The dorsalis pedis supplies the dorsum of the foot and continues on as the **arcuate artery** which issues the **dorsal metatarsal arteries** to the metatarsus of the foot. The dorsalis pedis is often palpated in patients with circulation problems of the leg to determine the circulatory efficiency to the limb as a whole.

• Palpate your own dorsalis pedis artery.

ACTIVITY 2

Locating Arteries on an Anatomical Chart or Model

Now that you have identified the arteries on Figures 32.2–32.6, attempt to locate and name them (without a reference) on a

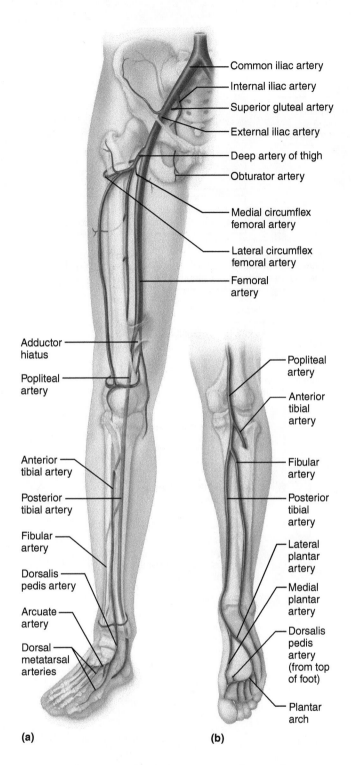

Common iliac artery

Internal iliac artery

Superior gluteal artery

External iliac artery

Deep artery of thigh

Obturator artery

Medial circumflex femoral artery

Lateral circumflex femoral artery

Femoral artery

Adductor hiatus

Popliteal artery

Anterior tibial artery

Posterior tibial artery

Fibular artery

Dorsalis pedis artery

Arcuate artery

Dorsal metatarsal arteries

Popliteal artery

Anterior tibial artery

Fibular artery

Posterior tibial artery

Lateral plantar artery

Medial plantar artery

Dorsalis pedis artery (from top of foot)

Plantar arch

(a)   **(b)**

FIGURE 32.6 Arteries of the right pelvis and lower limb. (a) Anterior view. **(b)** Posterior view.

large anatomical chart or three-dimensional model of the vascular system. ▬

Major Systemic Veins of the Body

Arteries are generally located in deep, well-protected body areas. However, many veins follow a more superficial course and are often easily seen and palpated on the body surface. Most deep veins parallel the course of the major arteries, and in many cases the naming of the veins and arteries is identical except for the designation of the vessels as veins. Whereas the major systemic arteries branch off the aorta, the veins tend to converge on the venae cavae, which enter the right atrium of the heart. Veins draining the head and upper extremities empty into the **superior vena cava,** and those draining the lower body empty into the **inferior vena cava.** Figure 32.7 is a schematic of the systemic veins and their relationship to the venae cavae to get you started.

Veins Draining into the Inferior Vena Cava

The inferior vena cava, a much longer vessel than the superior vena cava, returns blood to the heart from all body regions below the diaphragm (see Figure 32.7). It begins in the lower abdominal region with the union of the paired **common iliac veins,** which drain venous blood from the legs and pelvis.

Veins of the Lower Limbs

Each common iliac vein is formed by the union of the **internal iliac vein,** draining the pelvis, and the **external iliac vein,** which receives venous blood from the lower limb (Figure 32.8). Veins of the leg include the **anterior** and **posterior tibial veins,** which serve the calf and foot. The anterior tibial vein is a superior continuation of the **dorsalis pedis vein** of the foot. The posterior tibial vein is formed by the union of the **medial** and **lateral plantar veins,** and ascends deep in the calf muscles. It receives the **fibular vein** in the calf and then joins with the anterior tibial vein at the knee to produce the **popliteal vein,** which crosses the back of the knee. The popliteal vein becomes the **femoral vein** in the thigh; the femoral vein in turn becomes the external iliac vein in the inguinal region.

The **great saphenous vein,** a superficial vein, is the longest vein in the body. Beginning in common with the **small saphenous vein** from the **dorsal venous arch,** it extends up the medial side of the leg, knee, and thigh to empty into the femoral vein. The small saphenous vein runs along the lateral aspect of the foot and through the calf muscle, which it drains, and then empties into the popliteal vein at the knee (Figure 32.8b).

Veins of the Abdomen

Moving superiorly in the abdominal cavity (Figure 32.9), the inferior vena cava receives blood from the posterior abdominal wall via several pairs of **lumbar veins,** and from the right ovary or testis via the **right gonadal vein.** (The **left gonadal [ovarian or testicular] vein** drains into the left renal vein superiorly.) The paired **renal veins** drain the kidneys. Just above the right renal vein, the **right suprarenal vein** (receiving blood from the adrenal gland on the same side) drains into the inferior vena cava, but its partner, the **left suprarenal**

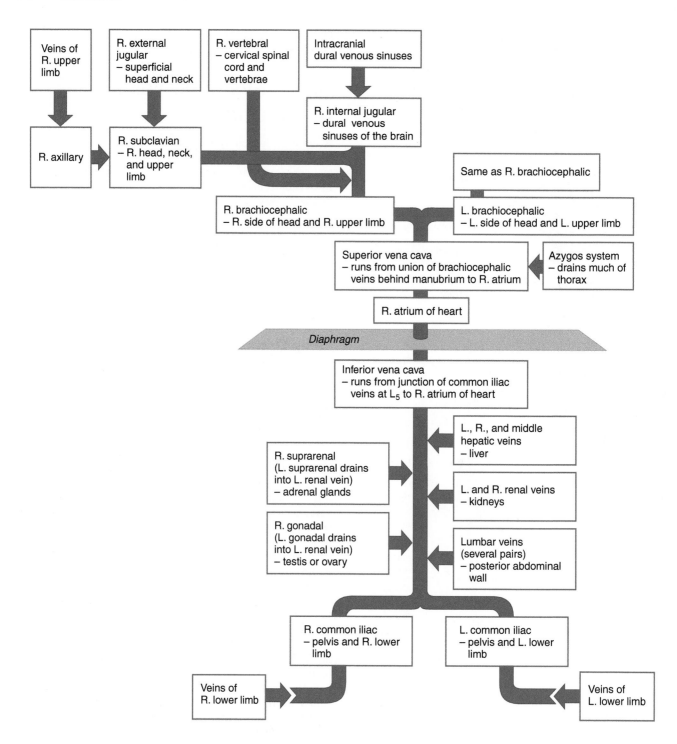

FIGURE 32.7 Schematic of systemic venous circulation.

vein, empties into the left renal vein inferiorly. The **hepatic veins** drain the liver. The unpaired veins draining the digestive tract organs empty into a special vessel, the hepatic portal vein, which carries blood to the liver to be processed before it enters the systemic venous system. (The hepatic portal system is discussed separately on page 484.)

Veins Draining into the Superior Vena Cava

Veins draining into the superior vena cava are named from the superior vena cava distally, _but remember that the flow of blood is in the opposite direction_.

Veins of the Head and Neck

The **right** and **left brachiocephalic veins** drain the head, neck, and upper extremities and unite to form the superior vena cava (Figure 32.10). Notice that although there is only one brachiocephalic artery, there are two brachiocephalic veins.

Branches of the brachiocephalic veins include the internal jugular, vertebral, and subclavian veins. The **internal jugular veins** are large veins that drain the superior sagittal sinus and other **dural sinuses** of the brain. As they run inferiorly, they receive blood from the head and neck via the **superficial temporal** and **facial veins.** The **vertebral veins** drain the posterior aspect of the head including the cervical vertebrae and spinal cord. The **subclavian veins** receive venous blood from the upper extremity. The **external jugular vein** joins the subclavian vein near its origin to return the venous drainage of the extracranial (superficial) tissues of the head and neck.

Veins of the Upper Limb and Thorax

As the subclavian vein traverses the axilla, it becomes the **axillary vein** and then the **brachial vein** as it courses along the posterior aspect of the humerus (Figure 32.11). The brachial vein is formed by the union of the deep **radial** and **ulnar veins** of the forearm. The superficial venous drainage of the arm includes the **cephalic vein,** which courses along the lateral aspect of the arm and empties into the axillary vein; the **basilic vein,** found on the medial aspect of the arm and entering the brachial vein; and the **median cubital vein,** which runs between the cephalic and basilic veins in the anterior aspect of the elbow (this vein is often the site of choice for removing blood for testing purposes). The **median antebrachial vein** lies between the radial and ulnar veins, and terminates variably by entering the cephalic or basilic vein at the elbow.

The **azygos system** (Figure 32.11) drains the intercostal muscles of the thorax and provides an accessory venous system to drain the abdominal wall. The **azygos vein,** which drains the right side of the thorax, enters the dorsal aspect of the superior vena cava immediately before that vessel enters the right atrium. Also part of the azygos system are the **hemiazygos** (a continuation of the **left ascending lumbar vein** of the abdomen) and the **accessory hemiazygos veins,** which together drain the left side of the thorax and empty into the azygos vein.

Identifying the Systemic Veins

Identify the important veins of the systemic circulation on the large anatomical chart or model without referring to the figures.

Special Circulations

Pulmonary Circulation

The pulmonary circulation (discussed previously in relation to heart anatomy on page 446) differs in many ways from systemic circulation because it does not serve the metabolic needs of the body tissues with which it is associated (in this case, lung

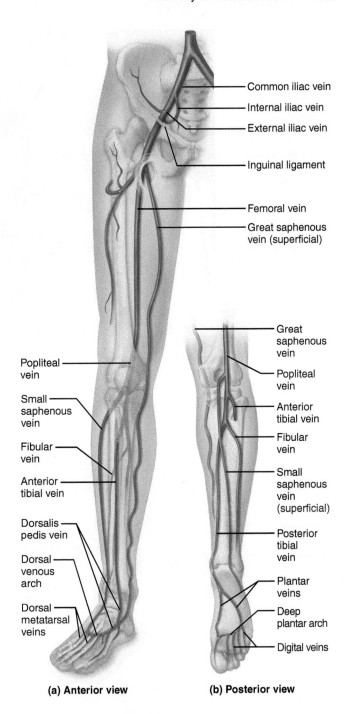

(a) Anterior view   (b) Posterior view

FIGURE 32.8 Veins of the right pelvis and lower limb. **(a)** Anterior view. **(b)** Posterior view.

tissue). It functions instead to bring the blood into close contact with the alveoli of the lungs to permit gas exchanges that rid the blood of excess carbon dioxide and replenish its supply of vital oxygen. The arteries of the pulmonary circulation are structurally much like veins, and they create a low-pressure bed in the lungs. (If the arterial pressure in the systemic circulation is 120/80, the pressure in the pulmonary artery is likely to be approximately 24/8.) The functional blood supply of the lungs is provided by the **bronchial arteries** (not shown), which diverge from the thoracic portion of the descending aorta.

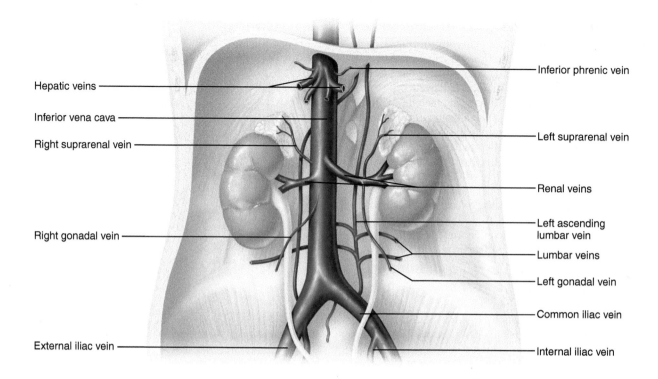

FIGURE 32.9 Venous drainage of abdominal organs not drained by the hepatic portal vein.

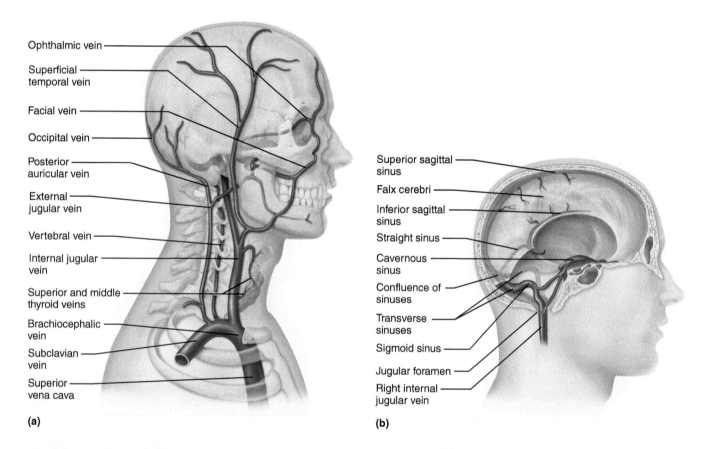

FIGURE 32.10 Venous drainage of the head, neck, and brain. **(a)** Veins of the head and neck, right superficial aspect. **(b)** Dural sinuses of the brain, right aspect.

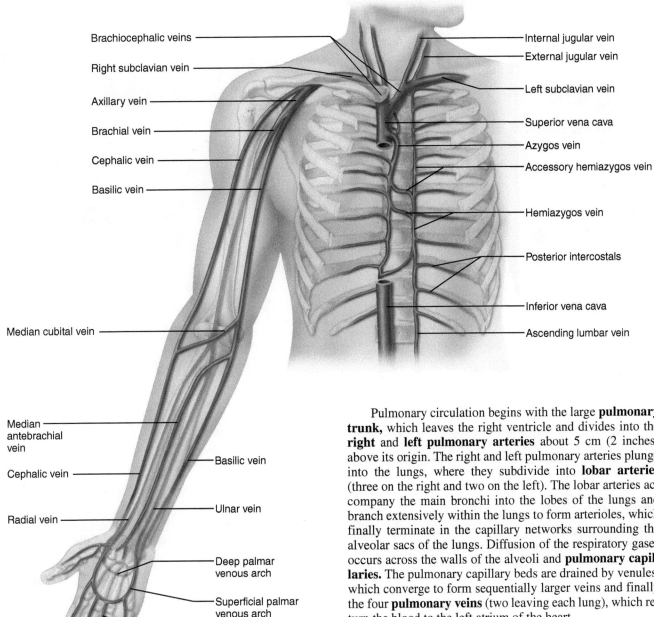

Brachiocephalic veins

Right subclavian vein

Axillary vein

Brachial vein

Cephalic vein

Basilic vein

Internal jugular vein

External jugular vein

Left subclavian vein

Superior vena cava

Azygos vein

Accessory hemiazygos vein

Hemiazygos vein

Posterior intercostals

Inferior vena cava

Ascending lumbar vein

Median cubital vein

Median antebrachial vein

Cephalic vein

Radial vein

Basilic vein

Ulnar vein

Deep palmar venous arch

Superficial palmar venous arch

Digital veins

FIGURE 32.11 Veins of the thorax and right upper limb. For clarity, the abundant branching and anastomoses of these vessels are not shown.

Pulmonary circulation begins with the large **pulmonary trunk,** which leaves the right ventricle and divides into the **right** and **left pulmonary arteries** about 5 cm (2 inches) above its origin. The right and left pulmonary arteries plunge into the lungs, where they subdivide into **lobar arteries** (three on the right and two on the left). The lobar arteries accompany the main bronchi into the lobes of the lungs and branch extensively within the lungs to form arterioles, which finally terminate in the capillary networks surrounding the alveolar sacs of the lungs. Diffusion of the respiratory gases occurs across the walls of the alveoli and **pulmonary capillaries.** The pulmonary capillary beds are drained by venules, which converge to form sequentially larger veins and finally the four **pulmonary veins** (two leaving each lung), which return the blood to the left atrium of the heart.

ACTIVITY 4

Identifying Vessels of the Pulmonary Circulation

As you read the descriptions below, find the vessels of the pulmonary circulation on Figure 32.12 and on an anatomical chart (if one is available). ■

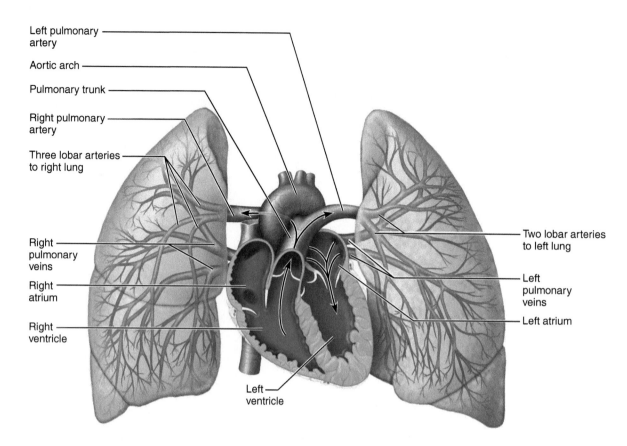

Left pulmonary artery

Aortic arch

Pulmonary trunk

Right pulmonary artery

Three lobar arteries to right lung

Right pulmonary veins

Right atrium

Right ventricle

Two lobar arteries to left lung

Left pulmonary veins

Left atrium

Left ventricle

FIGURE 32.12 The pulmonary circulation. The pulmonary arterial system is shown in blue to indicate that the blood carried is oxygen-poor. The pulmonary venous drainage is shown in red to indicate that the blood transported is oxygen-rich.

Fetal Circulation

In a developing fetus, the lungs and digestive system are not yet functional, and all nutrient, excretory, and gaseous exchanges occur through the placenta (see Figure 32.14a). Nutrients and oxygen move across placental barriers from the mother's blood into fetal blood, and carbon dioxide and other metabolic wastes move from the fetal blood supply to the mother's blood.

ACTIVITY 5

Tracing the Pathway of Fetal Blood Flow

Use Figure 32.13a and an anatomical chart (if available) to trace the pathway of fetal blood flow. Locate all the named vessels. Use Figure 32.13b to identify the named remnants of the foramen ovale and fetal vessels. ▆

Fetal blood travels through the umbilical cord, which contains three blood vessels: two smaller umbilical arteries and one large umbilical vein. The **umbilical vein** carries blood rich in nutrients and oxygen to the fetus; the **umbilical arteries** carry carbon dioxide and waste-laden blood from the fetus to the placenta. The umbilical arteries, which transport blood away from the fetal heart, meet the umbilical vein at the *umbilicus* (navel, or belly button) and wrap around the vein within the cord en route to their placental attachments. Newly oxygenated blood flows in the umbilical vein superiorly toward the fetal heart.

Some of this blood perfuses the liver, but the larger proportion is ducted through the relatively nonfunctional liver to the inferior vena cava via a shunt vessel called the **ductus venosus,** which carries the blood to the right atrium of the heart.

Because fetal lungs are nonfunctional and collapsed, two shunting mechanisms ensure that blood almost entirely bypasses the lungs. Much of the blood entering the right atrium is shunted into the left atrium through the **foramen ovale,** a flaplike opening in the interatrial septum. The left ventricle then pumps the blood out the aorta to the systemic circulation. Blood that does enter the right ventricle and is pumped out of the pulmonary trunk encounters a second shunt, the **ductus arteriosus,** a short vessel connecting the pulmonary trunk and the aorta. Because the collapsed lungs present an extremely high-resistance pathway, blood more readily enters the systemic circulation through the ductus arteriosus.

The aorta carries blood to the tissues of the body; this blood ultimately finds its way back to the placenta via the umbilical arteries. The only fetal vessel that carries highly oxygenated blood is the umbilical vein. All other vessels contain varying degrees of oxygenated and deoxygenated blood.

At birth, or shortly after, the foramen ovale closes and becomes the **fossa ovalis,** and the ductus arteriosus collapses and is converted to the fibrous **ligamentum arteriosum** (Figure 32.13b). Lack of blood flow through the umbilical vessels leads to their eventual obliteration, and the circulatory pattern becomes that of the adult. Remnants of the umbilical

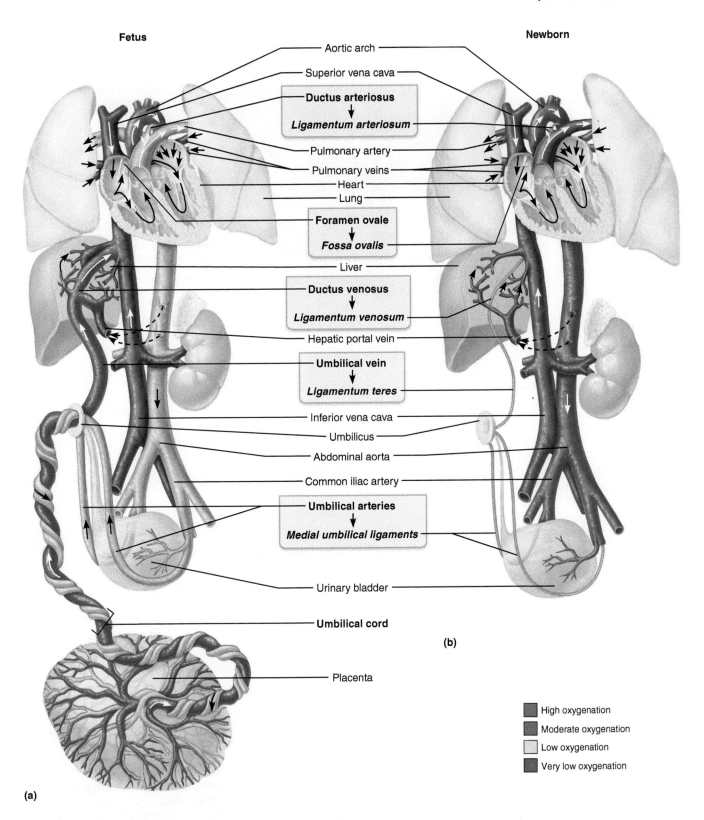

Fetus

Newborn

Aortic arch

Superior vena cava

Ductus arteriosus
↓
Ligamentum arteriosum

Pulmonary artery

Pulmonary veins

Heart

Lung

Foramen ovale
↓
Fossa ovalis

Liver

Ductus venosus
↓
Ligamentum venosum

Hepatic portal vein

Umbilical vein
↓
Ligamentum teres

Inferior vena cava

Umbilicus

Abdominal aorta

Common iliac artery

Umbilical arteries
↓
Medial umbilical ligaments

Urinary bladder

Umbilical cord

(b)

Placenta

High oxygenation

Moderate oxygenation

Low oxygenation

Very low oxygenation

(a)

FIGURE 32.13 Circulation in fetus and newborn. Arrows indicate direction of blood flow. Arrows in the blue boxes go from the fetal structure to what it becomes after birth. **(a)** Special adaptations for embryonic and fetal life. The umbilical vein (red) carries oxygen- and nutrient-rich blood from the placenta to the fetus. The umbilical arteries (pink) carry waste-laden blood from the fetus to the placenta. **(b)** Changes in the cardiovascular system at birth. The umbilical vessels are occluded, as are the liver and lung bypasses (ductus venosus and arteriosus, and the foramen ovale).

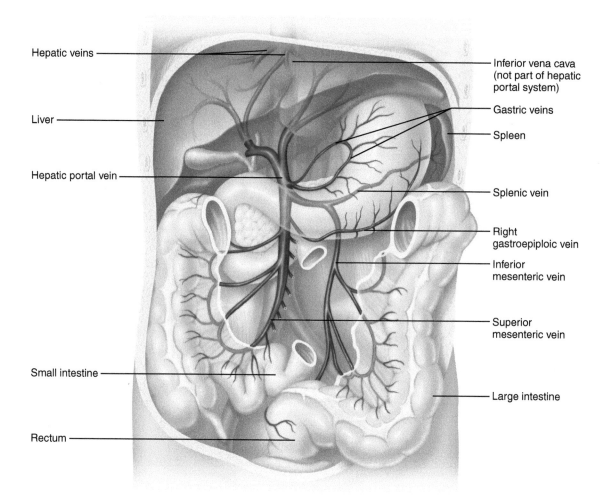

Hepatic veins

Liver

Hepatic portal vein

Small intestine

Rectum

Inferior vena cava (not part of hepatic portal system)

Gastric veins

Spleen

Splenic vein

Right gastroepiploic vein

Inferior mesenteric vein

Superior mesenteric vein

Large intestine

FIGURE 32.14 Hepatic portal circulation.

arteries persist as the **medial umbilical ligaments** on the inner surface of the anterior abdominal wall, of the umbilical vein as the **ligamentum teres** (or **round ligament**) of the liver, and of the ductus venosus as a fibrous band called the **ligamentum venosum** on the inferior surface of the liver.

Hepatic Portal Circulation

Blood vessels of the hepatic portal circulation drain the digestive viscera, spleen, and pancreas and deliver this blood to the liver for processing via the **hepatic portal vein.** If a meal has recently been eaten, the hepatic portal blood will be nutrient rich. The liver is the key body organ involved in maintaining proper sugar, fatty acid, and amino acid concentrations in the blood, and this system ensures that these substances pass through the liver before entering the systemic circulation. As blood percolates through the liver sinusoids, some of the nutrients are removed to be stored or processed in various ways for release to the general circulation. At the same time, the hepatocytes are detoxifying alcohol and other possibly harmful chemicals present in the blood, and the liver's macrophages are removing bacteria and other debris from the passing blood. The liver in

turn is drained by the hepatic veins that enter the inferior vena cava.

ACTIVITY 6

Tracing the Hepatic Portal Circulation

Locate on Figure 32.14, and on an anatomical chart of the hepatic portal circulation (if available), the vessels named below. ▆

The **inferior mesenteric vein,** draining the distal portions of the large intestine, joins the **splenic vein,** which drains the spleen and part of the pancreas and stomach. The splenic vein and the **superior mesenteric vein,** which receives blood from the small intestine and the ascending and transverse colon, unite to form the hepatic portal vein. The **left gastric vein,** which drains the lesser curvature of the stomach, drains directly into the hepatic portal vein.

For instructions on animal dissections, see the dissection exercises starting on page 697 in the cat, rat, and pig editions of this manual.

NAME _____

LAB TIME/DATE _____

Anatomy of Blood Vessels

Microscopic Structure of the Blood Vessels

1. Cross-sectional views of an artery and of a vein are shown here. Identify each; on the lines to the sides, note the structural details that enabled you to make these identifications:

(vessel type) _____   (vessel type) _____

_____   _____

(a)   (a)

_____   _____

(b)   (b)

Now describe each tunic more fully by selecting its characteristics from the key below and placing the appropriate key letters on the answer lines.

Tunica intima _____   Tunica media _____   Tunica externa _____

Key:

a. innermost tunic   d. especially thick in elastic arteries
b. most superficial tunic   e. contains smooth muscle and elastin
c. thin tunic of capillaries   f. has a smooth surface to decrease resistance to blood flow

2. Why are valves present in veins but not in arteries? _____

_____

_____

3. Name two events *occurring within the body* that aid in venous return.

_____ and _____

4. Why are the walls of arteries proportionately thicker than those of the corresponding veins? _____

_____

_____

Major Systemic Arteries and Veins of the Body

5. Use the key on the right to identify the arteries or veins described on the left.

Key: a.   anterior tibial

_____   1. the arterial system has one of these; the venous system has two

     b.   basilic

_____   2. these arteries supply the myocardium

     c.   brachial

_____, _____   3. two paired arteries serving the brain

     d.   brachiocephalic

_____   4. longest vein in the lower limb

     e.   celiac trunk

_____   5. artery on the dorsum of the foot checked after leg surgery

     f.   cephalic

_____   6. serves the posterior thigh

     g.   common carotid

_____   7. supplies the diaphragm

     h.   common iliac

_____   8. formed by the union of the radial and ulnar veins

     i.   coronary

_____, _____   9. two superficial veins of the arm

     j.   deep artery of the thigh

_____   10. artery serving the kidney

     k.   dorsalis pedis

_____   11. veins draining the liver

     l.   external carotid

_____   12. artery that supplies the distal half of the large intestine

     m.   femoral

_____   13. drains the pelvic organs

     n.   fibular

_____   14. what the external iliac artery becomes on entry into the thigh

     o.   great saphenous

_____   15. major artery serving the arm

     p.   hepatic

_____   16. supplies most of the small intestine

     q.   inferior mesenteric

_____   17. join to form the inferior vena cava

     r.   internal carotid

_____   18. an arterial trunk that has three major branches, which run to the liver, spleen, and stomach

     s.   internal iliac

     t.   phrenic

_____   19. major artery serving the tissues external to the skull

     u.   posterior tibial

     v.   radial

_____, _____, _____   20. three veins serving the leg

     w.   renal

_____   21. artery generally used to take the pulse at the wrist

     x.   subclavian

6. What is the function of the cerebral arterial circle (circle of Willis)?

     y.   superior mesenteric

     z.   vertebral

_____

7. The anterior and middle cerebral arteries arise from the _____ artery.

They serve the _____ of the brain.

8. Trace the pathway of a drop of blood from the aorta to the left occipital lobe of the brain, noting all structures through which

it flows. _____

_____

9. The human arterial and venous systems are diagrammed on this page and the next. Identify all indicated blood vessels.

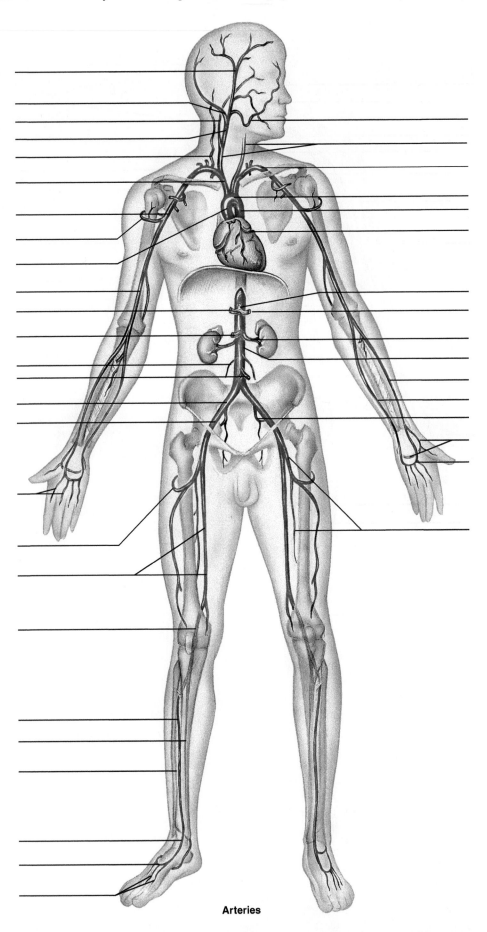

Arteries

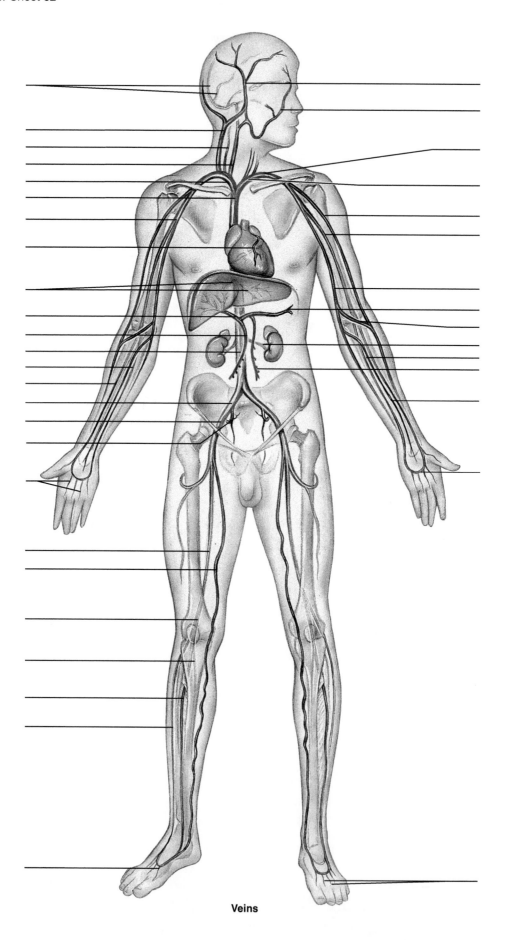

Veins

10. Trace the blood flow for each of the following situations.

a.   from the capillary beds of the left thumb to the capillary beds of the right thumb: _____

_____

_____

b.   from the mitral valve to the tricuspid valve by way of the great toe:

_____

_____

Pulmonary Circulation

11. Trace the pathway of a carbon dioxide gas molecule in the blood from the inferior vena cava until it leaves the bloodstream. Name all structures (vessels, heart chambers, and others) passed through en route.

_____

_____

12. Trace the pathway of oxygen gas molecules from an alveolus of the lung to the right ventricle of the heart. Name all structures

through which it passes. Circle the areas of gas exchange. _____

_____

13. Most arteries of the adult body carry oxygen-rich blood, and the veins carry carbon dioxide–rich blood.

How does this differ in the pulmonary arteries and veins? _____

_____

14. How do the arteries of the pulmonary circulation differ structurally from the systemic arteries? What condition is indicated

by this anatomical difference? _____

_____

Hepatic Portal Circulation

15. What is the source of blood in the hepatic portal system? _____

_____

16. Why is this blood carried to the liver before it enters the systemic circulation? _____

_____

17. The hepatic portal vein is formed by the union of (a) _____, which drains the _____,

_____, _____, _____, and (b) _____, which

drains the _____ and _____. The _____ vein, which drains the lesser

curvature of the stomach, empties directly into the hepatic portal vein.

18. Trace the flow of a drop of blood from the small intestine to the right atrium of the heart, noting all structures encountered

or passed through on the way. _____

_____

Fetal Circulation

19. For each of the following structures, first indicate its function in the fetus; and then note its fate (what happens to it or what it is converted to after birth). Circle the blood vessel that carries the most oxygen-rich blood.

Structure	Function in fetus	Fate
Umbilical artery		
Umbilical vein		
Ductus venosus		
Ductus arteriosus		
Foramen ovale		

20. What organ serves as a respiratory/digestive/excretory organ for the fetus? _____

The Metric System

Measurement	Unit and abbreviation	Metric equivalent	Metric to English conversion factor	English to metric conversion factor
Length	1 kilometer (km)	= 1000 (10^3) meters	1 km = 0.62 mile	1 mile = 1.61 km
	1 meter (m)	= 100 (10^2) centimeters	1 m = 1.09 yards	1 yard = 0.914 m
		= 1000 millimeters	1 m = 3.28 feet	1 foot = 0.305 m
			1 m = 39.37 inches	
	1 centimeter (cm)	= 0.01 (10^{-2}) meter	1 cm = 0.394 inch	1 foot = 30.5 cm
				1 inch = 2.54 cm
	1 millimeter (mm)	= 0.001 (10^{-3}) meter	1 mm = 0.039 inch	
	1 micrometer (μm) [formerly micron (μ)]	= 0.000001 (10^{-6}) meter		
	1 nanometer (nm) [formerly millimicron (mμ)]	= 0.000000001 (10^{-9}) meter		
	1 angstrom (Å)	= 0.0000000001 (10^{-10}) meter		
Area	1 square meter (m²)	= 10,000 square centimeters	1 m² = 1.1960 square yards	1 square yard = 0.8361 m²
			1 m² = 10.764 square feet	1 square foot = 0.0929 m²
	1 square centimeter (cm²)	= 100 square millimeters	1 cm² = 0.155 square inch	1 square inch = 6.4516 cm²
Mass	1 metric ton (t)	= 1000 kilograms	1 t = 1.103 ton	1 ton = 0.907 t
	1 kilogram (kg)	= 1000 grams	1 kg = 2.205 pounds	1 pound = 0.4536 kg
	1 gram (g)	= 1000 milligrams	1 g = 0.0353 ounce	1 ounce = 28.35 g
			1 g = 15.432 grains	
	1 milligram (mg)	= 0.001 gram	1 mg = approx. 0.015 grain	
	1 microgram (μg)	= 0.000001 gram		
Volume (solids)	1 cubic meter (m³)	= 1,000,000 cubic centimeters	1 m³ = 1.3080 cubic yards	1 cubic yard = 0.7646 m³
			1 m³ = 35.315 cubic feet	1 cubic foot = 0.0283 m³
	1 cubic centimeter (cm³ or cc)	= 0.000001 cubic meter = 1 milliliter	1 cm³ = 0.0610 cubic inch	1 cubic inch = 16.387 cm³
	1 cubic millimeter (mm³)	= 0.000000001 cubic meter		
Volume (liquids and gases)	1 kiloliter (kl or kL)	= 1000 liters	1 kL = 264.17 gallons	1 gallon = 3.785 L
	1 liter (l or L)	= 1000 milliliters	1 L = 0.264 gallons	1 quart = 0.946 L
			1 L = 1.057 quarts	
	1 milliliter (ml or mL)	= 0.001 liter = 1 cubic centimeter	1 ml = 0.034 fluid ounce	1 quart = 946 ml
				1 pint = 473 ml
			1 ml = approx. $\frac{1}{4}$ teaspoon	1 fluid ounce = 29.57 ml
			1 ml = approx. 15–16 drops (gtt.)	1 teaspoon = approx. 5 ml
	1 microliter (μl or μL)	= 0.000001 liter		
Time	1 second (s or sec)	= $\frac{1}{60}$ minute		
	1 millisecond (ms or msec)	= 0.001 second		
Temperature	Degrees Celsius (°C)		$°F = \frac{9}{5}(°C) + 32$	$°C = \frac{5}{9}(°F - 32)$

Credits

ILLUSTRATIONS

All illustrations are by Imagineering STA Media Services unless otherwise noted.

Exercise 1
1.1: Imagineering STA Media Services/Precision Graphics. 1.2, 1.4: Precision Graphics. 1.7: Adapted from Marieb and Mallatt, *Human Anatomy*, 3e, F1.10, © Benjamin Cummings, 2003.

Exercise 3
3.2–3.4, Activity 3: Precision Graphics.

Exercise 4
4.3: Tomo Narashima.

Exercise 5
5A.1: Precision Graphics.

Exercise 6
6A.2: Precision Graphics.

Exercise 7
7.1, 7.2, 7.7: Electronic Publishing Services, Inc.

Exercise 10
10.1–10.6, 10.8: Nadine Sokol.

Exercise 11
Table 11.1: Laurie O'Keefe.

Exercise 12
12.2a,b: Nadine Sokol.

Exercise 13
13.5: Precision Graphics.

Exercise 14
14.5: Electronic Publishing Services, Inc.

Exercise 15
15.1: Imagineering/Adapted from Martini, *Fundamentals of Anatomy & Physiology*, 4e, F11.1, Upper Saddle River, NJ: Prentice-Hall, © Frederic H. Martini, 1998.

Exercise 16
16A.1–16A.3: Precision Graphics. 16A.7–16A.9, 16A.13–16A.18, 16A.U1: Biopac Systems.

Exercise 17
17.1: Imagineering STA Media Services/Precision Graphics. 17.2, 17.5: Precision Graphics. 17.8a: Electronic Publishing Services, Inc.

Exercise 18
18A.2–18A.4: Precision Graphics.

Exercise 19
19.1, 19.5, 19.7–19.9: Electronic Publishing Services, Inc. 19.11b,c, 19.13a: Precision Graphics.

Exercise 20
20.4–20.7: Biopac Systems.

Exercise 21
21.2b: Electronic Publishing Services, Inc. 21.16–21.22: Biopac Systems.

Exercise 22
22.1: Electronic Publishing Services, Inc. 22.8, 22.9: Biopac Systems.

Exercise 24
24.1, 24.3a, 24.4a: Electronic Publishing Services, Inc. 24.7: Shirley Bortoli. 24.10, 24.11: Precision Graphics.

Exercise 25
25.1–25.3: Electronic Publishing Services, Inc./Precision Graphics.

Exercise 26
26.1, 26.2: Electronic Publishing Services, Inc.

Exercise 29
29A.2, 29A.5: Precision Graphics.

Exercise 30
30.1: Electronic Publishing Services, Inc./Precision Graphics. 30.2, 30.3a, 30.6: Electronic Publishing Services, Inc. 30.8: Precision Graphics.

Exercise 31
31.1: Electronic Publishing Services, Inc. 31.2, 31.4: Precision Graphics. 31.7–31.12: Biopac Systems.

Exercise 32
32.1: Adapted from Tortora and Grabowski, *Principles of Anatomy and Physiology*, 9e, F21.1, New York: Wiley, © Biological Sciences Textbooks and Sandra Reynolds Grabowski, 2000. 32.2, 32.3a, 32.4–32.12, 32.14: Electronic Publishing Services, Inc. 32.3b,c: Kristin Mount.

Exercise 33
33A.2: Precision Graphics. 33A.6–33A.8: Biopac Systems. 33A.9: Precision Graphics.

Exercise 34
34A.1, 34A.2, 34A.4: Precision Graphics. 34A.5: Biopac Systems. 34A.6a,b: Electronic Publishing Services, Inc.

Exercise 35
35A.8: Precision Graphics.

Exercise 36
36.1–36.5, 36.7: Electronic Publishing Services, Inc.

Exercise 37
37A.5, 37A.6: Precision Graphics. 37A.11, 37A.13, 37A.14: Biopac Systems.

Exercise 38
38.1–38.5, 38.8–38.10, 38.15: Electronic Publishing Services, Inc. 38.16: Electronic Publishing Services, Inc./Precision Graphics.

Exercise 39
Tables: Precision Graphics.

Exercise 40
40.1a, 40.2: Electronic Publishing Services, Inc.

Exercise 41
41A.1: Precision Graphics.

Exercise 42
42.1, 42.2a, 42.6: Electronic Publishing Services, Inc.

Exercise 43
43.1: Precision Graphics. 43.2: Electronic Publishing Services, Inc.

Exercise 44
44.1: Electronic Publishing Services, Inc.

Exercise 46
46.17: Precision Graphics.

Cat Dissection Exercises
CD1.1, CD3.1, CD3.3, CD7.1: Precision Graphics. CD2.1a, CD2.2a, CD3.2, CD4.2, CD4.3, CD6.1, CD7.2a, CD8.2a, CD9.1a: Kristin Mount.

Fetal Pig Dissection Exercises
Kristen Mount.

Rat Dissection Exercises
Imagineering STA Media Services.

PhysioEx Exercises
Opening Screens: Cadre Design. 18B.2, 34B.2: Precision Graphics.

PHOTOGRAPHS

Exercise 1
1.3 top: Jenny Thomas, Pearson Science. 1.3a: Howard Sochurek. 1.3b: James Cavallini/Photo Researchers. 1.3c: CNRI/Science Photo Library/Photo Researchers. 1.6b: Custom Medical Stock Photography.

Exercise 2
2.1–2.4a, 2.5b,c: Elena Dorfman, Pearson Science. 2.4b,c, 2.5a, 2.6a–c: David L. Bassett. 2.7: Carolina Biological Supply/Phototake.

Exercise 3
3.1: Leica. 3.5: Victor P. Eroschencko, Pearson Science.

Exercise 4
4.1: Don Fawcett and Science Source/Photo Researchers. 4.4a–f: Ed Reschke.

Exercise 5
5A.2a–c: Richard Megna/Fundamental Photographs. 5A.3a–c: David M. Philips/Photo Researchers.

Exercise 6
6A.3a: G. W. Willis/Visuals Unlimited. 6A.3b,f,h, 6A.5d,j,k: Allen Bell, University of New England. Pearson Science. 6A.3c,e, 6A.5c,f,i: Nina Zanetti, Pearson Science. 6A.3d, 6A.5a,b,g,h,l, 6A.7b: Ed Reschke. 6A.3g: R. G. Kessel and R. H. Kardon/ Visuals Unlimited. 6A.5e: Ed Reschke/Peter Arnold. 6A.6: Biophoto Associates/Photo Researchers. 6A.7a: Eric Graves/Photo Researchers. 6A.7c: Victor P. Eroschencko.

Exercise 7
7.2a: Ed Reschke/Peter Arnold. 7.3: Pearson Science. 7.5b: Carolina Biological Supply/ Phototake. 7.5d: Manfred Kage/Peter Arnold. 7.6a: Victor P. Eroschencko. 7.6b: From *Gray's Anatomy* by Henry Gray, © Churchill Livingstone, UK. 7.7a: Cabisco/Visuals Unlimited. 7.7b: John D. Cunningham/Visuals Unlimited. 7.RS.2: Marian Rice.

Exercise 8
8.2a–c: Steve Downing. 8.3: Pearson Science.

Exercise 9
9.4c: Ed Reschke/Peter Arnold. 9.5: Ed Reschke. 9.RS.2: Alan Bell, Pearson Science.

Exercise 10
10.4a,b, 10.5: Ralph T. Hutchings. 10.6c: Elena Dorfman, Pearson Science. 10.9c: From the David Bassett *Atlas of Human Anatomy*. 10.17b: Dissection by Shawn Miller, photography by Mark Nielsen and Alexa Doig. 10.18c: Pearson Science.

Exercise 11

11.5b: National Library of Medicine. Table 11.1: From *A Stereoscopic Atlas of Human Anatomy* by David L. Bassett.

Exercise 12

12.1: Jack Scanlon, Holyoke Community College, MA. 12.2c,d: R. T. Hutchings.

Exercise 13

13.6c: From *A Stereoscopic Atlas of Human Anatomy* by David L. Bassett. 13.7d: L. Bassett/ Visuals Unlimited. 13.8a: Mark Nielsen, University of Utah; Pearson Science. 13.8c: Video Surgery/ Photo Researchers.

Exercise 14

14.1a: Marian Rice. 14.3, 14.6: Victor P. Eroschencko, Pearson Science. 14.4: John D. Cunningham/Visuals Unlimited.

Exercise 15

15.4b: From *A Stereoscopic Atlas of Human Anatomy* by David L. Bassett. 15.5a, 15.8b, 15.9a: Dissection by Shawn Miller, photography by Mark Nielsen and Alexa Doig. 15.11f, L: Bassett/Visuals Unlimited. 15.13b: From the David Bassett *Atlas of Human Anatomy*.

Exercise 17

17.2c: Triarch/Visuals Unlimited. 17.3c: Don Fawcett/Photo Researchers. 17.4: Eroschencko's Interactive Histology. 17.6a: Carolina Biological Supply/Phototake. 17.6b: Thomas Deerinck, NCMIR/SPL/Photo Researchers. 17.6c: Nina Zanetti, Pearson Science. 17.8b: Victor P. Eroschencko, Pearson Science.

Exercise 19

19.2c: Robert A. Chase. 19.3: Ralph T. Hutchings/Visuals Unlimited. 19.4a: Ralph T. Hutchings. 19.5b: Pat Lynch/Photo Researchers. 19.6a,b, 19.7c: From *A Stereoscopic Atlas of Human Anatomy* by David L. Bassett. 19.10: A. Glauberman/Photo Researchers. 19.11a,d: Sharon Cummings, University of California, Davis; Pearson Science. 19.12, 19.13b, 19.14: Elena Dorfman, Pearson Science.

Exercise 20

20.1a: Alexander Tsiaras/Science Source/Photo Researchers.

Exercise 21

21.1b: From *A Stereoscopic Atlas of Human Anatomy* by David L. Bassett. 21.1c,d: L. Bassett/Visuals Unlimited. 21.4: Victor P. Eroschencko, Pearson Science. 21.7b: Ralph T. Hutchings.

Exercise 22

22.4–22.6: Richard Tauber, Pearson Science.

Exercise 23

23.1b: Kilgore College Biology Dept., Kilgore, Texas. 23.1c,d, 23.2b: Victor P. Eroschencko, Pearson Science.

Exercise 24

24.3b: From *A Stereoscopic Atlas of Human Anatomy* by David L Bassett. 24.4b: Ed Reschke/Peter Arnold. 24.5: Elena Dorfman, Pearson Science. 24.6b: Stephen Spector; courtesy of Charles Thomas, Kansas University Medical Center; Pearson Science. 24.12a,b: Richard Tauber, Pearson Science. 24.13: A. L. Blum/Visuals Unlimited.

Exercise 25

25.4: Victor P. Eroschencko, Pearson Science. 25.6a–c: Richard Tauber, Pearson Science. 25.8: I.

M. Hunter-Duvar, Department of Otolaryngology, The Hospital for Sick Children, Toronto.

Exercise 26

26.1b, 26.3: Victor P. Eroschencko, Pearson Science. 26.2d: Carolina Biological Supply/Phototake.

Exercise 27

27.3a: Michael Ross/Photo Researchers. 27.3b,d: Victor P. Eroschencko, Pearson Science. 27.3c: Carolina Biological Supply/Phototake. 27.3e: Benjamin Widrevitz, Natural Sciences Division, College of DuPage, Glen Ellyn, IL. 27.3f: Ed Reschke/Peter Arnold.

Exercise 29A

29A.3: Ed Reschke/Peter Arnold. 29A.4a–e: Nina Zanetti, Pearson Science. 29A.6a-c, 29A.7a–d: Elena Dorfman, Pearson Science. 29A.8: Meckes and Ottawa/Photo Researchers. 29A.9: Pearson Science.

Exercise 30

30.3b, 30.3d: From *A Stereoscopic Atlas of Human Anatomy* by David L. Bassett. 30.3c: Lennart Nilsson, *The Body Victorious*, New York: Dell, © Boehringer Ingelheim International GmbH. 30.7: Ed Reschke. 30.8a,b, 30.9: Wally Cash, Kansas State University; Pearson Science. 30.RS.3: Ed Reschke.

Exercise 32

32.1a: Gladden Willis/Visuals Unlimited. 32.3c: David L. Bassett.

Exercise 35A

35A.2: Ed Reschke/Peter Arnold. 35A.4b: Biophoto Associates/Photo Researchers. 35A.5c: LUMEN Histology, Loyola University Medical Education Network. 35A.6: John Cunningham/Visuals Unlimited.

Exercise 36

36.1a, 36.5b: From *A Stereoscopic Atlas of Human Anatomy* by David L. Bassett. 36.5a: Richard Tauber, Pearson Science. 36.6b: Victor P. Eroschencko, Pearson Science. 36.7a: Ed Reschke/Peter Arnold. 36.7b: Carolina Biological Supply/Phototake.

Exercise 37A

37A.3, 37A.4a,b: Elena Dorfman, Pearson Science.

Exercise 38

38.5b: From *Color Atlas of Histology* by Leslie P. Garner and James L. Hiatt, © Williams and Wilkins, 1990. 38.6a, 38.9a: Nina Zanetti, Pearson Science. 38.6b, 38.13: Victor P. Eroschencko, Pearson Science. 38.6c: Roger C. Wagner, Dept. of Biological Sciences, University of Delaware. 38.7a,c, 38.14a,b, 38.16b: From *A Stereoscopic Atlas of Human Anatomy* by David L. Bassett. 38.8d: LUMEN Histology, Loyola University Medical Education Network. 38.9b: Steve Downing: University of Kansas Medical Center, Department of Anatomy and Cell Biology.

Exercise 40

40.1b: Richard Tauber, Pearson Science. 40.3a: Ralph T. Hutchings. 40.6a,b, 40.7: Victor P. Eroschencko, Pearson Science.

Exercise 42

42.2b: Ed Reschke. 42.2c: From *A Stereoscopic Atlas of Human Anatomy* by David L. Bassett. 42.3: Harry Plymale. 42.4: Roger C. Wagner, University of Delaware. 42.7: Biodisc/Visuals Unlimited. 42.8: Victor P. Eroschencko, Pearson Science.

Exercise 43

43.2.b: Pearson Science. 43.3: M. Abbey/Visuals Unlimited. 43.5b: Ed Reschke. 43.6a–c: Victor P. Eroschencko, Pearson Science.

Exercise 45

45.1: CNRI/SPL/Photo Researchers. 45.2.1: Llewellyn/Uniphoto Picture Agency. 45.2.2: photos.com. 45.2.3, 45.2.4: Ogust/Image Works. 45.2.5: Boisvieux/Explorer/Photo Researchers. 45.2.6: Anthony Loveday, Pearson Science. 45.3: Carolina Biological Supply.

Exercise 46

46.1a,b, 46.3, 46.5, 46.7, 46.9–46.16, 46.18a–d, 46.19: John Wilson White, Pearson Science. 46.2: Jenny Thomas, Pearson Science.

Cat Dissection Exercises

CD1.2–CD1.13, CD2.3b CD4.1, CD4.4b, CD4.5, CD6.2, CD6.3, CD7.3, CD7.4, CD7.5b, CD8.1b, CD9.2b: Shawn Miller (dissection) and Mark Nielsen (photography), Pearson Science. CD2.1b, CD9.1b: Paul Waring, Pearson Science. CD2.2b, CD7.2b, CD8.2b: Elena Dorfman, Pearson Science. CD3.3b,c: Yvonne Baptiste-Szymanski, Pearson Science.

Fetal Pig Dissection Exercises

PD1.1, PD1.2: Jack Scanlon, Holyoke Community College, Pearson Science. PD1.3b, PD1.4b, PD1.5b, PD1.6b, PD1.7b, PD1.8b, PD2.1, PD4.1b, PD4.2b, PD4.3b, PD4.4b, PD5.1, PD5.2b, PD6.1b, PD6.2b, PD7.1b, PD7.2b, PD8.1b, PD8.2b: Elena Dorfman, Pearson Science. PD3.2b,c: Charles J. Venglarik, Pearson Science.

Rat Dissection Exercises

Robert J. Sullivan, Pearson Science.

TRADEMARK ACKNOWLEDGMENTS

3M is a trademark of 3M.

Adrenaline is a registered trademark of King Pharmaceuticals.

Albustix, Clinistix, Clinitest, Hemastix, Ictotest, Ketostix, and Multistix are registered trademarks of Bayer.

Betadine is a registered trademark of Purdue Products L. P.

Chemstrip is a registered trademark of Roche Diagnostics.

Coban is a trademark of 3M.

Harleco is a registered trademark of EMD Chemicals Inc.

Hefty® Baggies® is a registered trademark of Pactiv Corporation.

Landau is a registered trademark of Landau Uniforms.

Lycra is a registered trademark of INVISTA.

Macintosh, Power Macintosh and Mac OS X are registered trademarks of Apple Computer, Inc.

Novocain is a registered trademark of Sterling Drug, Inc.

Parafilm is a registered trademark of Pechiney Incorporated.

Sedi-stain is a registered trademark of Becton, Dickinson and Company.

Speedo is a registered trademark of Speedo International.

VELCRO® is a registered trademark of VELCRO Industries B. V.

Wampole is a registered trademark of Wampole Laboratories.

Windows is either a registered trademark or trademark of Microsoft Corporation in the United States and/or other countries.

Index